INTRODUCTION

I suppose the question I'm asked most often is how I came to dream up Modesty Blaise (and, of course, Willie Garvin, who is an essential part of her). The answer is I don't know but I sometimes suspect it happened the other way round, and Modesty Blaise dreamed me up as a tame biographer. Certainly in the early nineteen-sixties, with all that was to happen in the decade ahead, especially among women, Modesty Blaise must have been a character in search of an author; but she took her time about being born, for the gestation period was well over a year. That's how long I brooded over her while her character, qualities, abilities, virtues, vices, and history were gradually unfolded for me.

Once she had fully emerged, the totality of Willie Garvin followed about thirty seconds later, so I suspect she had him under wraps all the time. My greatest good fortune then was in being able to secure the peerless Jim Holdaway for the artwork. He at once lost his heart to Modesty, became great mates with Willie, loved drawing them in all varieties of mood and activity, and so made his own immense contribution to the strip.

Modesty Blaise and Willie Garvin first appeared in the London *Evening Standard* on Monday 13th May 1963 (or more accurately the strip first appeared that day but neither character was in the opening frames). There was no title frame to this story, which now strikes me as a rather odd omission, but perhaps I wanted all attention to be on the MODESTY BLAISE logo in the corner. Lacking a title, the story came to be called *La Machine* for identification purposes — though in fact I wouldn't dream of titling a story in a foreign language.

This book contains the first three Modesty Blaise adventures. The opener, *La Machine*, had to be a story which set pattern and style combined with a careful establishing of the essential history and characteristics of Modesty Blaise and Willie Garvin, in particular the relationship between them, a matter on which I've been put to many a long interrogation over the years.

The second story, *The Long Lever*, was designed to flesh out the characters more fully while telling a different kind of story, a tale of divided loyalties and failure, with a downbeat ending. I wanted to make clear that Modesty wasn't infallible, didn't always win and could suffer emotionally as well as physically.

The third story, *The Gabriel Set-Up*, contained an idea which I later discarded of having a running villain for Modesty and Willie to operate against. Since they never initiate trouble, only react to it, I have to start plotting any story

A previously unpublished sketch by Jim Holdaway.

by first creating the villains. And since strip cartoon is not a medium for subtle shades of grey, the villains can never be good-bad guys, they have to be bad-bad guys (or dolls) with no redeeming features. I thought a running villain (as Sherlock Holmes had Moriarty, and Robin Hood had the Sheriff of Nottingham) might be useful in the saga, hence Gabriel, who isn't dispatched at the end of the story, but lives to be villainous another day.

Following this, I used Gabriel in the first of the Modesty Blaise novels, again allowing him to survive the finale, but I used him only once more in a strip cartoon story. Then I went off the notion of a running villain because it seemed to me to be a bit of a cop-out, and I happily killed off Gabriel (at the hands of an even bigger villain) in the fourth of the novels, *A Taste For Death*.

When I was asked to write an introduction to these first three stories I winced in alarm because I felt I would be unable to remember any background to work done more than twenty years ago. But looking at the originals, marvelling and sighing over the work of the great Jim Holdaway, much of what I thought and felt at the time has come back to me, and I could easily go rambling on — but I won't. Let the stories speak for themselves. They are for your entertainment, and I hope you enjoy them.

PETER O'DONNELL. *August 1984.*

PETER O'DONNELL began writing professionally after leaving school just before World War 2. He has written in many media, but the newspaper strip format has showcased his talents best. He wrote Garth from 1953 to 1966 and Romeo Brown from 1956 to 1962. Since he created Modesty Blaise, which was first published in 1963, it has achieved international success. He has written 11 books based on the character, the strip is syndicated in 76 newspapers, and there has been one film and one television version of the character. Peter O'Donnell continues to write the Modesty Blaise strip and novels.

JIM HOLDAWAY was born in 1927. After various jobs ranging from rubber engraving to shoe advertising, he went freelance in 1950, specialising in comic strip work for Odhams and Farringdon Press. Among the long list of comics he contributed to were Captain Vigour, Comic Cuts, and Mickey Mouse Weekly. In 1956 he teamed up with Peter O'Donnell to work on Romeo Brown, and again in 1963 on Modesty Blaise. They continued to work as a team until Jim Holdaway's sudden and tragic death in 1970.

Published by Titan Books Ltd., 58 St. Giles High St., London WC2H 8LH, England. Distributed in the United Kingdom and the United States of America by Titan Distributors Ltd., P.O. Box 250, London E3 4RT, England. *Modesty Blaise* is © Express Newspapers Ltd. 1984. This edition is © Titan Books Ltd. 1984. Printed in Holland. ISBN 0 907610 34 X. *First edition January 1985.*

Modesty BLAISE
LA MACHINE
by PETER O'DONNELL and JIM HOLDAWAY

MODESTY BLAISE

A PENT-HOUSE OVERLOOKING HYDE PARK....

THE YOUNG LADY SEEMS TO DO HERSELF VERY WELL, FRASER

OUR DOSSIER PUTS HER PERSONAL FORTUNE AT OVER HALF A MILLION STERLING, SIR GERALD

AH... AN *UN*VIRTUOUS WOMAN WITH A PRICE ABOVE RUBIES, H'MM?

SHE ALWAYS BARRED THE VICE AND PROTECTION RACKETS .... ONE WOULD SEE *SOME* VIRTUE IN THAT, PERHAPS?

QUITE.... AND ONE WOULD BE GRATEFUL IF ONE WOULD NOT PICK HOLES IN ONE'S LITTLE QUIPS, FRASER...

1

MODESTY BLAISE

YES?

MISS MODESTY BLAISE? MY NAME IS TARRANT— MAY I HAVE A FEW WORDS WITH YOU?

ON WHAT SUBJECT?

WOULD— AH—*MURDER* BE ALL RIGHT?

YES, CERTAINLY, DO COME UP.... SIR GERALD

2

MODESTY BLAISE

IT WAS NICE MEETING YOU, CARTER D. SANFORD THE THIRD --- GOODNIGHT!

NOW, MODESTY, NOT SO FAST...

...I DON'T GET STOOD UP THAT EASY, HONEY! WHEN WE DUCKED OUT OF THAT PARTY AND YOU ASKED ME ALONG FOR A DRINK, I FIGURED...

YOU GOT YOUR SUMS WRONG.... I'M NOT THAT BORED!

I'VE A VISITOR COMING UP IN THE LIFT— YOU CAN TAKE IT DOWN!

NO DICE! JUST GIVE THE JERK A DRINK AND GET RID OF HIM!

3

MODESTY BLAISE

MODESTY BLAISE

MODESTY BLAISE

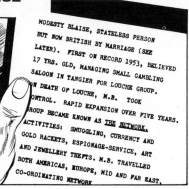

MODESTY BLAISE

MODESTY BLAISE

Modesty Blaise.

IT'S A VERY GOOD DOSSIER, SIR GERALD— BUT MAINLY SPECULATION, OF COURSE!

OH, QUITE! NO *PROOF* OF ANY ILLEGALITIES— AND BESIDES, I'M NOT A POLICEMAN, YOU KNOW

SO?

AH, THANK YOU! WELL, MISS BLAISE... TO COME TO THE POINT, I THINK WE CAN USE YOU...

NOBODY... *NOBODY* USES ME, SIR GERALD. I DECIDED *THAT* IN A REFUGEE CAMP, WHEN I WAS TWELVE!

MODESTY BLAISE

YOUR MARRIAGE IN BEIRUT TO THE LATE MR. TURNER—THAT WAS PURELY TO OBTAIN BRITISH NATIONALITY?

VERY PURELY, I ASSURE YOU..

YE-E-ES... WELL, I'M AFRAID IT WASN'T VALID. WE HAVE A CERTIFICATE OF HIS *EARLIER MARRIAGE*, YOU SEE!

YOU PAID HIM FOR *NOTHING*, MISS BLAISE... YOU'RE STILL A STATELESS PERSON, AND COULD BE DEPORTED AS UNDESIRABLE!

MODESTY BLAISE

SO YOU'LL DEPORT ME... UNLESS I AGREE TO DO SOME JOB FOR YOU—IS THAT IT?

OH, BY NO MEANS...

...THIS MARRIAGE CERTIFICATE IS THE ONLY EVIDENCE WHICH COULD TAKE AWAY YOUR BRITISH NATIONALITY..

THERE! NOW I'VE COMMITTED A CIVIL OFFENCE, SHOCKED POOR FRASER, DESTROYED MY ONLY HOLD OVER YOU— AND ENJOYED A RIDICULOUSLY DRAMATIC GESTURE!

YOU'RE A CLEVER MAN, SIR GERALD... HOW DID YOU KNOW I'M A COMPULSIVE PAYER OF DEBTS?

MODESTY BLAISE

WHAT IS THIS JOB YOU WANT ME TO DO? YOU MENTIONED MURDER...

YES. MY CHAPS ATTACHED TO NATO WANT TO BREAK THE ORGANISATION CALLED 'LA MACHINE'... IT'S BEING USED TOO MUCH BY OUR POTENTIAL ENEMIES..

AH, *LA MACHINE?* THEY SPECIALISE IN BESPOKE MURDER. JUST PAY YOUR MONEY AND NAME YOUR VICTIM— SATISFACTION GUARANTEED!

YOU THINK I CAN HELP?

I THINK YOU MAY HAVE FOUND LUXURIOUS RETIREMENT VERY TEDIOUS... IF SO, COME AND SEE ME TOMORROW, AND WE'LL TALK ABOUT A JOB, MISS BLAISE...

MODESTY BLAISE

MODESTY BLAISE

MODESTY BLAISE

MODESTY BLAISE

MODESTY BLAISE by PETER O'DONNELL

36

DO YOU HAVE ANY PARTICULAR PLAN FOR US, SIR GERALD?

AH, NOW YOU'RE *TESTING* ME, MY DEAR! PLEASE CREDIT ME WITH A MEASURE OF SAGACITY...

I KNOW THAT THE *ONLY* WAY YOU'LL TACKLE THIS JOB IS YOUR *OWN* WAY— I SIMPLY OFFER YOU ANY HELP MY ORGANISATION CAN GIVE

YOU WERE RIGHT ABOUT 'IM, PRINCESS— I MUST SAY IT'S A PLEASURE TO WORK FOR A GAFFER WHO'S GOT ALL 'IS MARBLES

MODESTY BLAISE by PETER O'DONNELL

HAVE YOU SOME KIND OF PLAN IN MIND?

THIS FILE SAYS *LA MACHINE* WORKS MAINLY BY *APPROACHING* LIKELY CLIENTS... THEY HAVE THE KIND OF INFORMATION THAT HELPS TO SPOT POTENTIAL *CUSTOMERS*

SO I'LL SET MYSELF UP AS A GOOD PROSPECTIVE CLIENT... WITH WILLIE GARVIN AS THE MAN I WANT MURDERED

AHH...*YES!* YES, INDEED! YOU'LL NEED TIME TO ESTABLISH A PLAUSIBLE BACKGROUND OF ENMITY, OF COURSE

THREE WEEKS, WE RECKON

37

MODESTY BLAISE by PETER O'DONNELL

SO YOU'LL INVITE AN APPROACH FROM *LA MACHINE* TO MURDER MR. GARVIN FOR YOU... NOW WHAT ABOUT DETAILS?

YOU CAN LEAVE ALL THAT TO US, SIR GERALD

WITH EVERY CONFIDENCE, MY DEAR... I'LL JUST GIVE YOU THE METHOD FOR CONTACTING MY HEAD FELLOW IN FRANCE, IF YOU NEED TO

HE'LL BE TOLD TO TAKE ORDERS FROM YOU AND FROM MR. GARVIN FOR THIS EXERCISE

WOULD YOU MIND CALLING ME WILLIE, SIR G? I MEAN, WE'RE MORE OR LESS MATES NOW, AREN'T WE?

38

MODESTY BLAISE by PETER O'DONNELL

IS THERE ANYTHING YOU WANT TO DRAW FROM THE ARMOURY?

THANK YOU, NO— WE SUPPLY OUR OWN TOOLS, AND WILLIE DOESN'T LIKE GUNS ANYWAY

PROBABLY BECAUSE HE'S THE WORLD'S WORST SHOT!

AH, THEY'RE ALL RIGHT FOR WESTERNS — BUT BUSINESS-WISE THEY'RE MOSTLY A DRAG

WILLIE SAYS A GUN MAKES A MAN TOO CONFIDENT— AND I MUST SAY HE'S PROVED IT ONCE OR TWICE WITH GREAT SUCCESS

I'M GLAD YOU AVOID OVER- CONFIDENCE— IT WOULDN'T DO, NOT AGAINST *LA MACHINE*...

39

MODESTY BLAISE by PETER O'DONNELL

THE RUMOUR SPREADS AND HARDENS...

YOU HAVE TALKED TO MODESTY BLAISE—AND NOW YOU ADVISE ME THAT WE KEEP *OUT* OF THE NEW *NETWORK*? BUT WE COMBINED VERY PROFITABLY WITH HER BEFORE, JELAL

I SENSED A DIFFERENCE IN HER...THE COOLNESS IS NO LONGER *REAL*, AND HER NERVES ARE SHOWING...THIS COME-BACK IS AN OBSESSION—SHE WANTS IT, YET FEARS IT

AND SO, AFTER THREE WEEKS IN A PARIS APARTMENT...

THE STORY-LINE'S WELL SET, PRINCESS—WE CAN STAGE THE BIG PUNCH-UP TOMORROW NIGHT

OKAY, WILLIE,.. AND REMEMBER IT MUSTN'T JUST *LOOK* REAL, IT'S GOT TO *BE* REAL

44

MODESTY BLAISE by PETER O'DONNELL

LE GANT ROUGE—A NIGHT-CLUB WHERE THE ELITE OF THE PARIS UNDERWORLD GATHER

LOOK ROUND SLOWLY IN A MOMENT... *IT IS MODESTY BLAISE*

THEY SAY SHE WILL NOT TALK TO GARVIN, AND HE GROWS ANGRY!

GARVIN IS FORMIDABLE,.. *I* WOULD NOT CROSS HIM... BUT HE WILL BE A FOOL TO CROSS *THAT ONE!*

MON DIEU— HE IS HERE!

45

MODESTY BLAISE by PETER O'DONNELL

WELL, WELL... I'VE BIN CHASING ROUND TRYIN' TO 'AVE A TALK WITH YOU FOR LONG ENOUGH, PRINCESS

YOU'VE MADE A DAMN NUISANCE OF YOURSELF!

WHY NOT? *YOU* TOOK US OUT OF THE BUSINESS—AND IF YOU'RE MOVING BACK, THEN *I* WANT IN LIKE BEFORE

I WON'T NEED AN OFFICE-BOY— I'M DOING THIS *ALONE!*

IT LOOKS AS IF—

TAIS-TOI! I AM TRYING TO CATCH A WORD OR TWO! WHY THE DEVIL MUST GARVIN TALK IN THAT COCKNEY ENGLISH WHEN HE SPEAKS FRENCH LIKE A PARISIEN?

46

MODESTY BLAISE by PETER O'DONNELL

LOOK, I'LL GIVE YOU THE SCORE, MISS MODESTY RUDDY BLAISE—EITHER YOU TAKE ME IN WITH YOU, *OR* I'LL STOP YOU DEAD!

THE UNDERWORLD CLIENTELE OF LE GANT ROUGE SEE MODESTY'S TEMPER SNAP!

DON'T THREATEN *ME*, YOU SCUT!

WELL NOW...! IT LOOKS LIKE I'LL 'AVE TO SHOW YOU I'M NOT JUST *TALKING*...

47

MODESTY BLAISE
by PETER O'DONNELL

YOU'VE GOT EVERYTHING SET THE WAY WE ARRANGED?

SURE, PRINCESS... I'M SHACKED UP WITH LITTLE PERNOD MIMI, DOWN IN MONTMARTRE, AND GOING TO SEED FAST ON BOOZE

NOW I'M OFF TO SHUT MESELF UP FOR A THREE-DAY BENDER... SO WHOEVER'S BRIEFED TO KNOCK ME OFF WILL 'AVE TO COME AN' GET ME!

DON'T LET THAT POOR LITTLE SOUSE GET HURT, WILLIE

SHE WON'T... I'M ALWAYS CONSIDERATE WITH ME GIRL FRIENDS, PRINCESS

56

MODESTY BLAISE
by PETER O'DONNELL

MONTMARTRE, THREE A.M., TWO DAYS AFTER MODESTY BLAISE HAS COMMISSIONED WILLIE GARVIN'S DEATH...

THE LIGHT IS STILL ON...

WHEN PERNOD MIMI WAKES AT NIGHT, SHE LIKES TO FIND THE BOTTLE EASILY... AND SO DOES GARVIN NOW, IT SEEMS

MORE SIMPLE FOR US THEN... LET'S GET IT DONE WITH

A BUZZER SOUNDS SOFTLY UNDER WILLIE GARVIN'S PILLOW, TWICE...

TWO OF 'EM, ON THE STAIRS NOW...

57

MODESTY BLAISE
by PETER O'DONNELL

WILLIE... ARE YOU GETTING A DRINK? ONE FOR ME TOO, PLEASE

LATER, MA PETITE—YOU HAVE TO SLEEP SOUNDLY FOR A LITTLE WHILE NOW...

...UNDER THE BED, NICE AND SAFE

uhh!

THE KILLERS MOVE SILENTLY INTO THE OUTER ROOM

58

MODESTY BLAISE
by PETER O'DONNELL

THE BEDROOM DOOR OPENS SILENTLY ON WILLIE'S DRUNKEN SNORES

GARVIN IS THERE, BUT NOT PERNOD MIMI. FOR THE MOMENT—STAY BY THE DOOR IN CASE SHE COMES

USING A CHIV, THEN...

IN WILLIE'S HAND IS HIDDEN A SWITCH CONNECTED TO THE LIGHT...

59

MODESTY BLAISE
by PETER O'DONNELL

I DON'T LIKE IT... YOU'VE STUCK YOUR NECK OUT A *MILE!*

DON'T BE DAMN SILLY, WILLIE LOVE.... *I* DIDN'T FUSS WHEN *YOU* WERE WAITING FOR THE CHOPPER

STOP ROUND THE CORNER FROM FRANK BRETT'S FLAT— YOU'RE GOING TO LIE LOW THERE, WILLIE, AND I MEAN *LIE LOW!*

SO WHO STANDS BY TO TAIL YOU WHEN YOU'RE SNATCHED?

NOBODY... WE'VE GOT TO BE SMARTER THAN THAT

72

MODESTY BLAISE
by PETER O'DONNELL

*M*ORNING.... AND THE AREA-MANAGER OF *LA MACHINE* FINDS THE MESSAGE FROM MODESTY IN HIS LOCKED SAFE

JANINE!

M'SIEU?

DELAY MY ELEVEN O'CLOCK APPOINTMENT— I HAVE TO GO OUT FOR A FEW MINUTES

BRETT, OF NATO INTELLIGENCE, GETS A CALL FROM HIS FRENCH OPPOSITE NUMBER

THAT WAS NIMEAU —HE'S PUT A TAP ON THE MAN'S PHONE, WILLIE

ROUVET WON'T BE FOOL ENOUGH TO TALK FROM 'IS OFFICE... YOU'VE GOT A CLOCK WANTS MENDING 'ERE, FRANK

73

MODESTY BLAISE
by PETER O'DONNELL

I STILL SAY THAT WHEN *LA MACHINE* GRAB MODESTY FROM THAT HOTEL SHE'S MOVED TO, WE OUGHT TO TAIL THEM

YOUR FRENCH MATES 'AVE GOT A STATIC NETWORK OF POLICE LAID OUT TO REPORT ALL ALONG ANY ROUTE THEY MIGHT TAKE 'ER

NETS HAVE HOLES, WILLIE

74

I KNOW... BUT THE FRENCH POLICE ARE RED 'OT ON THIS KIND OF CAPER... AND ANYWAY, WE GOT TO PLAY IT THE WAY MODESTY SAID

MODESTY BLAISE
by PETER O'DONNELL

*F*OR TWO DAYS MODESTY DOES NOT LEAVE THE HOTEL, AND AT LAST...

EXCUSE ME, MAM'SELLE, THIS NOTE WILL INTRODUCE ME— I AM TO ARRANGE A MEETING WITH SOME FRIENDS OF MINE YOU WISH TO SEE

AH, YES...

"TWO GUNS WITHIN THREE METRES OF YOU— WALK WITH ME TO THE CAR OUTSIDE OR THEY WILL SHOOT TO KILL"

YOU HAVE GONE TO NEEDLESS TROUBLE, M'SIEU

PERHAPS— BUT MY FRIENDS WISHED IT SO— SHALL WE GO?

75

MODESTY BLAISE
by PETER O'DONNELL

LA MACHINE'S HIRELINGS TAKE MODESTY BLAISE FROM THE HOTEL

A HUNDRED METRES AWAY

IT BEGINS, RAOUL... SHE IS GETTING INTO A GREY CITROEN... WITH THREE MEN—

GET THE NUMBER OF IT

76

FIVE MINUTES LATER...

NIMEAU ON THE BLOWER THEY'VE GOT HER, WILLIE! HE'LL BE ROUND FOR US IN THE CONTROL CAR ANY MINUTE, SO YOU CAN QUIT DISMANTLING MY CHATTELS AT LAST

MODESTY BLAISE
by PETER O'DONNELL

AFTER SEVERAL HOURS IN THE CAR, MODESTY SPEAKS FOR THE FIRST TIME

HOW MUCH LONGER?

SHUT YOUR MOUTH, DOLL— WE'RE NOT PAID TO TALK

REPORTING FROM REFERENCE E.12— THE CAR TURNS RIGHT TOWARDS PEYRINS

77

TEN MILES BEHIND...

UNDERSTOOD

YOUR NICE STRAIGHT ROADS WERE MADE FOR THIS, NIMEAU

IT'S TOO EASY.... I DON'T LIKE IT

MODESTY BLAISE
by PETER O'DONNELL

MY EARS HAVE STARTED PRICKLING — THAT'S A SURE SIGN SOMETHING'S GOING TO GO SOUR

EARS? THIS IS THE FAMOUS ENGLISH HUMOUR, PERHAPS?

I'M NOT BEING FUNNY, NIMEAU... I'M JUST BEING SCARED

SCARED FOR MODESTY BLAISE? YOU HAVEN'T WORRIED SO FAR, WILLIE— WHY NOW?

BECAUSE MY EARS HAVE STARTED PRICKLING, YOU GREAT STEAMING NIT!

78

MODESTY BLAISE
by PETER O'DONNELL

TOWARDS DAWN, THE CITROEN SWINGS INTO A SMALL COURTYARD IN THE LITTLE VILLAGE OF TARLIER

WELL? WHAT NOW?

I WARNED YOU ABOUT ASKING QUESTIONS, DOLL

LOUIS— CHECK AGAIN FOR A HIDDEN WEAPON, THEN PUT A ROPE ON HER

79

MODESTY BLAISE
by PETER O'DONNELL

OVERLOOKING THE VILLAGE OF TARLIER STANDS THE MONASTERY KNOWN AS *LA RETRAITE*

NO PROBLEMS? NOBODY TRIED TO TAIL THE CAR FROM PARIS?

NO, THEY WERE POSITIVE ON THAT... AND SHE HAS GIVEN NO TROUBLE SO FAR

AH, GOOD MORNING! SO YOU ARE MODESTY BLAISE, WHO HAS A PROPOSITION FOR US?

MODESTY BLAISE
by PETER O'DONNELL

*M*ID-MORNING IN THE POLICE STATION AT TARLIER

NO WORD OF THE CAR SINCE DAWN... IT SEEMS THAT GARVIN'S EARLY-WARNING EARS WERE RIGHT IN SENSING TROUBLE, MON VIEUX!

THE CITROEN CAME *INTO* TARLIER, BUT DIDN'T COME *OUT*— SO WHERE THE HELL IS IT?

NOT ANYWHERE IN THE VILLAGE, M'SIEU, WE HAVE CHECKED DISCREETLY—BUT *THOROUGHLY!*

SUPPOSE THEY HANDED MODESTY OVER *HERE* SOMEWHERE... THEN THE CITROEN HEADED BACK ON THE SAME ROAD THAT *WE'D* JUST COME IN BY— NO ONE WOULD BE LOOKING FOR THEM *THERE* ANY LONGER...

MODESTY BLAISE
by PETER O'DONNELL

SHE *WOULD* PLAY IT THIS WAY, WILLIE... AND NOW, GOD HELP HER, *LA MACHINE* HAS GOT HER... YOU WERE RIGHT TO BE SCARED

THAT'S OVER, MATEY...

I ONLY GET EDGY WHEN THINGS ARE *GOING* WRONG, NOT ONCE THEY'VE GONE... AND THEY ALWAYS DO, SOMEWHERE, SHE KNOWS THAT WELL ENOUGH

MODESTY'S BEEN UNDER THE CHOPPER BEFORE, AND COME OUT ALL RIGHT— THEY'VE GOT A TIGER BY THE TAIL THERE

LET'S GO AND TALK TO THE LOCAL BAKER

BAKER?

MODESTY BLAISE
by PETER O'DONNELL

THE BAKER'S UP AND ABOUT EARLIER THAN ANYONE— HE COULD HAVE SEEN SOMETHING

IT IS A CHANCE... I'LL TALK TO HIM

STONE IN MY SHOE

WILLIE RISES, AND WALKS ON *PAST* THE BAKERY

HEEL OF MODESTY'S SHOE— IT WAS JAMMED IN THE WHEEL OF THAT VAN, NIMEAU! LET'S CHECK ON THIS BAKER BEFORE WE START TALKING TO HIM

MODESTY BLAISE by PETER O'DONNELL

THAT IS WHERE LAGRONNE DELIVERS BREAD BEFORE DAWN EACH DAY... *LA RETRAITE*, A PLACE OF REST FOR AILING AND ELDERLY MONKS

ELDERLY MONKS! YOU'RE WASTING TIME, WILLIE — WE SHOULD BE SQUEEZING LAGRONNE! HE'S THE LINK-MAN

IF SO, I DON'T WANT HIM SCARED... NOT YET ANYWAY

GO ON ABOUT *LA RETRAITE*, MON VIEUX— WOULD A TOURIST BE PERMITTED TO VISIT IT?

AH, NO... IT IS MOST PRIVATE

84

MODESTY BLAISE by PETER O'DONNELL

FATHER MARASIN WAS SENT FOUR YEARS AGO TO TAKE OVER *LA RETRAITE*, HE CAME FROM ALGERIA...

...THE ONLY SURVIVOR OF A MONASTERY DESTROYED DURING THE FIGHTING

SATISFIED, WILLIE? *LA MACHINE* CAN'T BE BASED *THERE!*

YEAH, IT'S IMPOSSIBLE... AND THAT'S JUST WHAT MAKES IT FAVOURITE IN MY BOOK, FRANKIE BOY

85

MODESTY BLAISE by PETER O'DONNELL

IN THE HIGH-WALLED GROUNDS OF LA RETRAITE, FRAIL AND ELDERLY MONKS MOVE SLOWLY TO THE CHAPEL FOR PRAYER...

AND IN THE QUARTERS OF FATHER MARASIN...

GET ME A QUICK DRINK, CASTELLE... I'M ON IN FIVE MINUTES

AND KEEP OUT OF THE BLAISE WOMAN'S CELL — YOU HEAR?

I HEAR, MON COLONEL

86

MODESTY BLAISE by PETER O'DONNELL

WE'LL LEAVE HER TO SWEAT TILL TONIGHT, WITHOUT GOING NEAR HER — THEN IT WON'T TAKE LONG TO BREAK HER DOWN

NO ONE CAN WAIT TWELVE HOURS TO GET HURT WITHOUT STARTING TO CRACK A LITTLE... AND SHE *KNOWS* SHE'S GOING TO GET HURT ALL RIGHT

BUT IN A WINDOWLESS CELL, REMOTE FROM THE MAIN LIVING-QUARTERS OF THE MONASTERY, MODESTY BLAISE LIES WITHDRAWN FROM ALL FEARS... ASLEEP

87

MODESTY BLAISE
by PETER O'DONNELL

MODESTY BLAISE
by PETER O'DONNELL

MODESTY BLAISE
by PETER O'DONNELL

MODESTY BLAISE
by PETER O'DONNELL

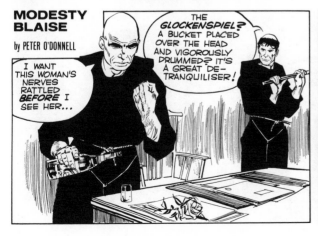

MODESTY BLAISE
by PETER O'DONNELL

GET UP... DON'T SPEAK... AND DON'T GET STUBBORN

FIVE MINUTES LATER, IN THE BELL-TOWER

ENJOY THE MUSIC, MY LITTLE CABBAGE, IT'S JUST STARTING... AND REMEMBER THIS IS ONLY THE **OVERTURE** TO A LONG, HARD NIGHT

THE FIRST SHATTERING STROKE OF THE BELL-HAMMER REVERBERATES THROUGH THE TOWER

92

MODESTY BLAISE
by PETER O'DONNELL

93

AS THE CLANGOUR OF THE GREAT BELL GROWS MORE TERRIBLE, MODESTY BLAISE FILLS HER LUNGS TO CAPACITY, EXHALES FULLY ...AGAIN AND YET AGAIN

STEADY... CAN'T RUSH THE KNOCKOUT TRICK! TWO MINUTES FULL DEEP-BREATHING...

THE BREATH HELD SHARPLY...EVERY MUSCLE OF CHEST AND STOMACH TENSED TO SUDDEN, FIERCE RIGIDITY...

...AND WITH THE SWIFT DRAIN OF BLOOD FROM THE HEAD, MODESTY SAGS LIMPLY IN A DEEP FAINT

MODESTY BLAISE
by PETER O'DONNELL

*WILLIE GARVIN KEEPS WATCH ON **LA RETRAITE***

94

THE BELL'S STOPPED... RECKON THEY'LL SOON BE TUCKED UP FOR THE NIGHT — MOST OF 'EM, ANYWAY

'ALLO...! THAT'S LAGRONNE THE BAKER'S VAN — HE'S OPENING UP TO DRIVE IN THE SIDE-WAY

WILLIE MATE, YOU'RE POINTING THE RIGHT WAY... BUT DON'T HANG AROUND TOO LONG... THAT VAN COULD BE FOR TAKIN' THE PRINCESS **OUT**, WHEN THEY'VE FINISHED WITH HER...

MODESTY BLAISE
by PETER O'DONNELL

95

CASTELLE SHOULD HAVE THE WOMAN READY FOR QUESTIONING NOW, YOU'RE JUST IN TIME, LAGRONNE

BON! I DIDN'T WANT **HIM** TO HAVE ALL THE FUN... HE'S A GREEDY SWINE

AH... MAM'SELLE BLAISE! HOW DID YOU ENJOY OUR BELL-RINGING?

WHAT BELL-RINGING? I CAN'T HAVE BEEN LISTENING

IF YOU'RE THE BOSS OF **LA MACHINE**, LET ME TELL YOU YOUR ORGANISATION STINKS, MY FRIEND — YOU COULD CERTAINLY DO WITH SOME FRESH BLOOD IN IT

MODESTY BLAISE
by PETER O'DONNELL

YOUR MURDER-MACHINE IS SLIPPING — I COMMISSIONED YOU TO KILL WILLIE GARVIN, AND YOU SENT TWO DUMB THUGS WHO COULDN'T COPE WITH HIM *ASLEEP* AND *DRUNK!*

I'M NOT YET SATISFIED ON THAT. BUT IF OUR AREA-MANAGER *DID* USE INADEQUATE LABOUR, THEN LAGRONNE HERE, MY LIAISON OFFICER, WILL PASS ON A SEVERE REPRIMAND

AND NOW, MAM'SELLE, THERE ARE ONE OR TWO POINTS YOU MUST HELP US CLEAR UP BEFORE WE KILL YOU...

96

MODESTY BLAISE
by PETER O'DONNELL

MY SOLE INTEREST IN YOU IS TO LEARN *HOW* YOU TRACED MY AREA-MANAGER IN PARIS, AND IF YOU *ALONE* KNOW HIS IDENTITY

I'LL BE GLAD TO TELL YOU

WHEN YOU HAVE GIVEN A *PLAUSIBLE* ANSWER, WE SHALL INFLICT PAIN... YOUR NEXT ANSWER WILL BE *NEARER* THE TRUTH ...AND WE SHALL CONTINUE UNTIL YOU CAN *ONLY* TELL THE TRUTH...

WE ARE EXPERTS IN KNOWING WHEN THAT POINT IS REACHED

YES? I'D LIKE TO KNOW YOUR REFERENCES

97

MODESTY BLAISE
by PETER O'DONNELL

I AM A DEAD MAN, MAM'SELLE... COLONEL RAUT, LATE OF THE FOREIGN LEGION, LATE OF THE O.A.S. — KILLED IN ACTION FOUR YEARS AGO

I HARDLY THOUGHT YOU WERE IN HOLY ORDERS

NO... BUT I SPENT A SHORT PERIOD TRAINING FOR THEM IN MY YOUTH, WHICH MADE THIS MASQUERADE EASIER FOR ME

AND THE MAN WHOSE PLACE YOU TOOK?

FATHER MARASIN? I KILLED HIM IN ALGERIA AND TOOK HIS IDENTITY... AND THESE TWO ARE OLD COMRADES OF MINE, EX-SERGEANT CASTELLE AND EX-LEGIONNAIRE LAGRONNE

WILLIE GARVIN MOVES IN.... 98

MODESTY BLAISE
by PETER O'DONNELL

WHY SHOULD THEY? I RUN *LA RETRAITE* TO THE ENTIRE SATISFACTION OF MY CLERICAL SUPERIORS...

IN FOUR YEARS NOBODY HAS SUSPECTED THAT YOU'RE *NOT* THE REAL FATHER MARASIN?

AND BEFORE I KILLED MARASIN I KNEW HIS FACE WAS VIRTUALLY UNKNOWN OUTSIDE THAT MONASTERY IN ALGERIA OF WHICH HE WAS THE *SOLE* SURVIVOR

LET'S GET ON WITH IT, MON COLONEL — I HAVEN'T MADE ANYONE TALK SINCE THE O.A.S....

99

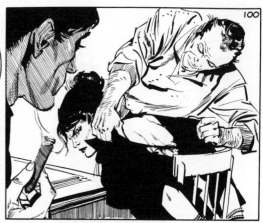

MODESTY BLAISE
by PETER O'DONNELL

OUTSIDE THE GENDARMERIE...

SO LAGRONNE, THE BAKER, *WAS* IN IT! WHO ELSE, MON VIEUX?

NOT SURE—GARVIN ONLY GAVE ME THE BONES OF IT ON THE PHONE... BUT THERE ARE THREE DEAD

SEEMS THEY'D JUST STARTED DAMAGING MODESTY WHEN HE ARRIVED... AND OUR WILLIE WOULDN'T LIKE THAT ONE BIT

THREE! NOT EASY WITHOUT A GUN...

MODESTY HERSELF TOOK THE BIG BOY... THAT INJURED HAND OF HERS WAS A FAKE, NIMEAU! SHE HAD A PEN-GUN FIXED UNDER THE BANDAGES...

MODESTY BLAISE
by PETER O'DONNELL

THOSE FILES, FRANK—FULL DETAILS OF *LA MACHINE'S* ORGANISATION, CONTACTS, CLIENTS—YOU CAN'T MISS

THIS MESS WILL HAVE TO BE CLEARED UP BEFORE THE MONKS ARE ABOUT TOMORROW... AND YOU'D BETTER RING THE CHURCH AUTHORITIES ABOUT SENDING SOMEONE TO TAKE CHARGE HERE—

LEAVE IT ALL TO US, MODESTY...YOU TAKE THE CAR AND GET SOME SLEEP—THERE'S A LITTLE HOTEL BEHIND THE GENDARMERIE

SLIP THIS ON, PRINCESS... I THINK YOU'RE FEELING A BIT CHILLY

MODESTY BLAISE
by PETER O'DONNELL

WELL...! IT WORKED OUT VERY NICE, REALLY...

WILLIE, I—I'M SORRY... GIVE ME A MOMENT TO—TO STEADY UP...

AH, WHY THE *HELL* DO I... ALWAYS S-SNIVEL ONCE A JOB'S OVER...?

ONLY THE TOUGH JOBS, PRINCESS, AN' YOU GOT TO UNWIND SOME WAY... I *LIKE* IT MESELF—IT'S, YOU KNOW, NICE AN' *WOMANLY*

THAT'S RIGHT, YOU 'AVE A GOOD CRY...NO ONE'LL EVER KNOW BUT MRS. GARVIN'S LITTLE WILLIE, SO WHAT'S IT MATTER?

MODESTY BLAISE
by PETER O'DONNELL

*A*FTER FIVE MINUTES, MODESTY SITS UP AND DRIES HER TEARS

AHH...THANKS FOR THE SHOULDER TO UNWIND ON... I FEEL A NEW WOMAN NOW

RIGHT, THEN 'OP IN THE CAR AND WE'LL GET YOU TO THE 'OTEL FOR A GOOD NIGHT'S KIP, EH?

WILLIE, LOVE... HOW DO *YOU* UNWIND?

WELL, I'M TOO BIG TO 'AVE A CRY...

SO I RELY ON ME LITTLE ADDRESS-BOOK, PRINCESS

YES...THERE'S A LOT TO BE SAID FOR THOSE GOOD OLD-FASHIONED REMEDIES

MODESTY BLAISE
by PETER O'DONNELL

IN THE PENT-HOUSE OF MODESTY BLAISE, A WEEK AFTER THE DESTRUCTION OF THE MURDER-GROUP CALLED *LA MACHINE*

WELL... DO YOU ALWAYS WELCOME YOUR OPERATIVES HOME WITH *FLOWERS*, SIR GERALD?

ONLY WHEN THEY'RE FEMALE—AND WORK ON AN HONORARY BASIS, WITHOUT PAYMENT

HOW ARE YOU, MODESTY? I'VE HAD BRETT'S REPORT—YOU TOOK A LOT OF PUNISHMENT

NO LASTING DAMAGE... IN FACT I FEEL FINE! IT'S A MISTAKE TO QUIT WORKING WHEN YOU'VE KNOWN NOTHING ELSE ALL YOUR LIFE

112

MODESTY BLAISE
by PETER O'DONNELL

I'D *LIKE* TO MAKE A PAYMENT TO WILLIE GARVIN—BUT WILL HE ACCEPT?

NO. WILLIE'S LOADED... AND ANYWAY HE'LL TELL YOU HE ONLY WORKS FOR ME, SIR GERALD

THAT'S NOT *MY* VIEW, YOU UNDERSTAND? IT'S HIS

YOURS FAITHFULLY WILLIE GARVIN, H'MM? WELL, AT LEAST I MUST *THANK* THE SCOUNDREL...

I THINK HE'S GONE AWAY FOR A LITTLE HOLIDAY—JUST TO UNWIND, YOU KNOW

WHERE CAN I FIND HIM?

113

MODESTY BLAISE
by PETER O'DONNELL

MAY I COME TO YOU AGAIN—IF THERE'S A JOB THAT CALLS FOR YOUR RATHER SPECIAL TALENTS?

I HOPE YOU WILL

I *NEED* TO BUY YOUR WARES FROM TIME TO TIME, SIR GERALD... I'M HOOKED, AND I KNOW IT NOW

MY DREAM OF RETIRING WAS JUST A PIPE-DREAM...

114

YOU KNEW THAT, WHEN YOU FIRST CAME TO ME, DIDN'T YOU?

OH YES... AND I MAKE USE OF IT BECAUSE I MUST... BUT I ALLOW MYSELF THE RATHER SAD SATISFACTION OF *DISLIKING* MYSELF FOR IT...

Modesty BLAISE
THE LONG LEVER
by PETER O'DONNELL and JIM HOLDAWAY

RIO DE JANEIRO, WHERE A SCIENTIFIC COMMITTEE OF UNESCO HAS GATHERED TO DISCUSS RADIO-COMMUNICATIONS IN SOUTH AMERICA

KOSSUTH JUST VANISHED? WHAT THE HELL DO YOU MEAN?

MODESTY BLAISE
by PETER O'DONNELL

MEN OF THE UNITED STATES CENTRAL INTELLIGENCE AGENCY

WHAT HAPPENED?

TEN MINUTES AGO I CHECKED KOSSUTH GETTING INTO THE ELEVATOR BY HOTEL RECEPTION — BRADY WAS ON THE FOURTH FLOOR TO CHECK HIM INTO HIS ROOM

WHEN THE ELEVATOR ARRIVED NO DR. KOSSUTH! THEY MUST HAVE GRABBED HIM WHEN IT STOPPED AT THE THIRD, I GUESS ...BUT HOW COULD THEY GET HIM AWAY, UNCONSCIOUS?

UNCONSCIOUS?

YOU KNOW HIS BACKGROUND! A GUN WOULDN'T STOP HIM YELLING — HE'D SOONER GET SHOT THAN LET THEM TAKE HIM BACK

116

MODESTY BLAISE
by PETER O'DONNELL

SO THEY'VE GOT DOCTOR KOSSUTH... BUT THEY'RE STILL A LONG WAY FROM HOME! LET'S GO, DAVE

GO WHERE?

INCLUDING US, WE'VE GOT FOUR MEN TO COVER ALL RIO DE JANEIRO — YOU AIM TO SURROUND THE PLACE?

WE'LL PLAY MY HUNCH AND CHECK ON DE SÀ, THAT MILLIONAIRE GUY KOSSUTH SPENT SOME TIME WITH

IT'S AN ANGLE... I HEARD DE SÀ'S YACHT'S SAILING TONIGHT

117

MODESTY BLAISE by PETER O'DONNELL

FOUR OF US TO GUARD ONE GUY... THE JOB SHOULD HAVE BEEN A MILK-RUN! I TELL YOU, FELLER — WASHINGTON'S GOING TO JUST *LOVE* US FOR LETTING THEIR DR. KOSSUTH GET SNATCHED

*S*OME THIRTY HOURS LATER... THE LOUNGE OF RAND'S CLUB IN PALL MALL...

YOU CHOOSE THE WINE, WILLIE — WE'VE A GOOD CELLAR HERE, EH, MITCHELL?

YES INDEED, SIR GERALD

118

YOU WOULDN'T HAVE A RED *VIN ORDINAIRE* — A NICE ROUGH 'UN?

I'LL SEND OUT FOR A BOTTLE WITH PLEASURE, SIR... I THINK I KNOW JUST THE THING

MODESTY BLAISE by PETER O'DONNELL

HOW DO YOU *DO* IT, WILLIE? I MEAN, ORDER *VIN ORDINAIRE* AND WIN OLD MITCHELL'S APPROVAL! HE'D HAVE *FROZEN* ME!

I NEVER THOUGHT ABOUT IT, SIR G. — MUST BE A GIFT I SUPPOSE...

OR MAYBE I GOT THE KNACK FROM MODESTY... SHE DRINKS THE ROUGH RED, AN' WAITERS RUN ROUND IN CIRCLES FOR HER

AH, YES ...MODESTY

I'M GLAD WE HAD THIS LUNCH-DATE FIXED — A RUSH JOB'S COME UP WHICH *MAY* BE QUITE NON-INFLAMMABLE, BUT MAY *NOT*... I'D LIKE YOU TO TAKE IT *SOLO*, WILLIE

119

MODESTY BLAISE by PETER O'DONNELL

WHAT KIND OF CAPER IS IT?

MY AMERICAN COLLEAGUES ARE IN A HOLE... THEY'VE ASKED ME TO HELP IF POSSIBLE. BUT THEY DON'T THINK I CAN,

FOR SUFFICIENT REASON, I PARTICULARLY WANT TO PULL SOMETHING OUT OF THE HAT FOR THEM ON THIS — AND I'VE A GOOD NOTION HOW IT CAN BE DONE

IF IT NEEDED TWO, I'D GO TO MODESTY BLAISE... BUT IT DOESN'T, AND THAT'S WHY I'M ASKING IF YOU'LL GO SOLO, WILLIE

OKAY... AS LONG AS MODESTY SAYS SO

120

MODESTY BLAISE by PETER O'DONNELL

BUT IF WE MENTION THIS TO MODESTY, SHE'LL WANT TO BE IN ON IT! DAMMIT WILLIE, I THOUGHT YOU'D BE *GLAD* TO KEEP HER FROM BEING PUT AT RISK

I'D NEVER TAKE A DEAD LIBERTY LIKE THAT, SIR G! MODESTY BLAISE IS HER OWN BOSS — *AND* MINE, WHEN IT COMES TO A CAPER

NOT IN *HER* VIEW, WILLIE, YOU KNOW THAT — SO WHY LET HER DECIDE FOR YOU ON THIS?

BECAUSE IT *WORKS*... IT'S WORKED FROM THE FIRST DAY I MET HER, WHEN SHE BOUGHT ME OUT OF JAIL IN SAIGON...

121

MODESTY BLAISE
by PETER O'DONNELL

I WAS A RIGHT VILLAIN IN THOSE DAYS... MODESTY WAS ONLY TWENTY, BUT WELL IN THE BIG-TIME... SHE SPRANG ME FROM JAIL, TOOK ME TO A BAR, AN' SAT LOOKIN' AT ME...

"THEY TELL ME YOU'RE A RAT, WILLIE GARVIN," SHE SAYS, "BUT I THINK THERE'S A MAN INSIDE YOU TRYING TO GET OUT—A MAN I COULD USE"

SEEMED LIKE A PRINCESS, SHE DID... AND I KNEW SHE'D STARTED EVEN LOWER IN THE MUD THAN *ME*!... WHAT'S MORE, I RECKONED SHE WAS TALKIN' THE COLD TRUTH

MODESTY BLAISE
by PETER O'DONNELL

TO CUT A LONG STORY SHORT, MODESTY TOOK ME BACK TO TANGIER WITH HER—AND IN SIX MONTHS SHE WAS TRUSTING ME LIKE HER RIGHT ARM

THAT COULDN'T 'VE HAPPENED WITH THE **OLD** WILLIE GARVIN, BELIEVE ME...

ALL RIGHT, WILLIE... SO YOU'LL ONLY TACKLE A JOB ON MODESTY'S SAY-SO—BECAUSE IT'S A WINNING SYSTEM...

SHALL WE RING AND FIND OUT IF SHE'LL BE AT HOME THIS AFTERNOON?

MODESTY BLAISE
by PETER O'DONNELL

WILLIE?... I'M IN THE WORK ROOM

RIGHT, PRINCESS

HALLO, SIR GERALD—MAY I FINISH THIS FIRST AND REMEMBER MY MANNERS LATER?

MY DEAR, I MUCH PREFER AN INFORMAL WELCOME

WHEN WILLIE PHONED HE SAID IT WAS URGENT, SO YOU'D BETTER GO AHEAD AND TALK—I CAN LISTEN

MODESTY BLAISE
by PETER O'DONNELL

DR. ALEXIUS KOSSUTH, AGE FORTY-FOUR, HUNGARIAN BY BIRTH, PRE-WAR REFUGEE FROM NAZIS, STUDENT IN GREECE, CAUGHT THERE WHEN GERMANS INVADED IN '41, HELD AT KALYROS INTERNMENT CAMP—

KALYROS? MY GOD, THAT HELL-HOLE...

WERE **YOU** THERE? DID YOU KNOW HIM?

I SPENT SOME MONTHS THERE... I'M NOT SURE WHEN... I WAS ABOUT SIX, AND ALONE BY THEN... ALL I REMEMBER IS WONDERING WHOSE FOOD I COULD STEAL SAFELY

MODESTY BLAISE
by PETER O'DONNELL

THERE'S ONE THIN HOPE OF GETTING KOSSUTH BACK ...THE C.I.A. PEOPLE HAVE A SUSPICION, A *HUNCH* ONLY, THAT HE'S A PRISONER ABOARD *THE FLAMENCO*...

THE YACHT OF RAPHAEL DE SÁ, BRAZILIAN MILLIONAIRE, NOW TWO DAYS OUT FROM RIO, BOUND FOR FREETOWN — THEN THE MED. PERHAPS, AND THROUGH THE BOSPHORUS TO AN IRON CURTAIN PORT

A PRO-RED MILLIONAIRE?

DE SÁ IS PRO NOTHING BUT DE SÁ, AND HIS FINANCIAL EMPIRE IS SHAKY— FOR *ENOUGH* MONEY, HE'D DO ANYTHING

MODESTY BLAISE
by PETER O'DONNELL

I SUPPOSE THE YANKS CAN'T TAKE ACTION BECAUSE—

PAUSE FOR COFFEE, WILLIE— HERE, TRY THIS ON YOUR GIRL FRIEND, IT MIGHT BE EVEN BETTER THAN THE RIGHT BRAND OF CHOCOLATES

IT'S THE CLOSE SEASON JUST NOW, BUT THIS'LL KEEP— AN' THANKS, PRINCESS

IT'S A GARNET... CAMEO SCULPTURED... *SUPERB!*

MY GOD, WILLIE, SHE CAN'T *MEAN* YOU TO GIVE THIS TO-AH- TO SOMEBODY?

SHE DON'T GIVE WITH STRINGS, Y'KNOW! BUT YOU NEEDN'T SWEAT— I GOT A COLLECTION OF 'EM THAT YOU CAN COME AN' SEE SOMETIME

MODESTY BLAISE
by PETER O'DONNELL

YOU'D BETTER KNOW NOW, SIR GERALD— I WANT TO BE IN ON THIS KOSSUTH AFFAIR... *UNLESS* IT WOULD WEAKEN WHATEVER PLAN YOU HAVE IN MIND

I CAN'T PRETEND IT WOULD

YOU HAVE A SPECIAL, FELLOW-FEELING FOR KOSSUTH, I THINK... BECAUSE HE'S VIRTUALLY BEEN A LIFE LONG REFUGEE?

YES

WELL, THAT'S IT, SIR G... I DON'T GO SOLO, IT'S EITHER BOTH OF US OR NEITHER

MODESTY BLAISE
by PETER O'DONNELL

THE AMERICANS *DAREN'T* HAVE THEIR NAVY STOP DE SÁ'S YACHT TO LOOK FOR KOSSUTH— NOT UNLESS THEY CAN BE ONE HUNDRED PERCENT SURE OF FINDING HIM

THAT MEANS GETTING SOMEBODY ABOARD WHO CAN FIND OUT— AND THEN PASS THE WORD AT A PORT OF CALL

NICE RAISINS, WILLIE?

M'MM, LOVELY

THEY THOUGHT *WE* MIGHT BE ABLE TO GET A MAN ABOARD AT FREETOWN...

HOW? BY MESMERISM? IF THE HUNCH IS RIGHT, DE SÁ WILL TAKE ON SUPPLIES BY TENDER AND YOU WOULDN'T GET A *MOUSE* ABOARD

MODESTY BLAISE
by PETER O'DONNELL

NOW I KNOW YOU LIKE TO DEVISE YOUR *OWN* PLANS, MODESTY, BUT—

I'LL ALWAYS BUY ONE OFF THE PEG IF IT'S A GOOD FIT, SIR GERALD... HAVE *YOU* AN IDEA FOR GETTING US ABOARD DE SÄ'S YACHT?

WELL... THERE *ARE* THESE ODD PEOPLE WHO CRUISE ROUND THE WORLD IN LITTLE SAILING-BOATS... AND THEY *COULD* STRIKE TROUBLE AND HAVE TO TAKE TO A RUBBER DINGHY...

WE COULD CERT'NLY 'VE USED YOU IN THE OLD DAYS, SIR G! HONEST YOU GOT THE MAKINGS OF A LOVELY CROOK

134

MODESTY BLAISE
by PETER O'DONNELL

THE AMERICANS ARE KEEPING TABS ON *THE FLAMENCO* WITH A HIGH-FLYING PLANE... WE CAN PLACE YOU WHERE SHE'S BOUND TO PASS WITHIN A FEW MILES

WE BOTH GOT A GOOD TAN, PRINCESS— BUT WE OUGHTER BE A BIT *BURNT* FROM A DAY OR SO IN AN OPEN DINGHY

A LITTLE FRYING UNDER LAMPS OUGHT TO COVER THAT, WILLIE, LOVE

WHAT ABOUT DOCUMENTS? SHIP'S PAPERS?

I HAVE THE VERY BEST FORGERS, MY DEAR

135

MODESTY BLAISE
by PETER O'DONNELL

IT'S A WORKABLE PLAN... ALL WE NEED NOW IS A DETAILED COVER-STORY AND BACKGROUND FOR WILLIE AND ME

'OW DO WE *GET* TO MID-ATLANTIC, SIR G?

YOU FLY TO BRITISH GUIANA ..."*BRIGA TRANSPORT*" HAVE A FLYING-BOAT THERE WHICH CAN DO THE JOB, AND THEY'RE WILLING TO CHARTER IT

WE'LL NEED A PHOTOGRAPH OF DR. KOSSUTH ...I WANT TO KNOW WHAT HE LOOKS LIKE

136

MODESTY BLAISE
by PETER O'DONNELL

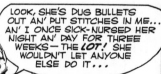

WILLIE...I SUPPOSE MODESTY REALISES THAT WE'LL HAVE TO CAST YOU AS HUSBAND AND WIFE ON THIS OPERATION— AND MAKE IT STICK?

'COURSE SHE DOES

LOOK, SHE'S DUG BULLETS OUT AN' PUT STITCHES IN ME... AN' I ONCE SICK-NURSED HER NIGHT AN' DAY FOR THREE WEEKS — THE *LOT!* SHE WOULDN'T LET ANYONE ELSE DO IT...

SO IF YOU DO GET US ABOARD *THE FLAMENCO* AS MR. AN' MRS., WE'RE NOT LIKELY TO GIVE OURSELVES AWAY BY ACTING STUPID

137

MODESTY BLAISE
by PETER O'DONNELL

In the hour before dawn, a flying-boat lands in the South Atlantic, near the equator

ALL SET, SQUIRE? YOU'RE A HUNDRED ODD MILES NORTH-EAST OF THE POSITION WE GOT BY RADIO TEN MINUTES AGO

THANKS, MATEY... LET'S GET THIS DINGHY OUT

138

I DON'T KNOW WHAT THE HELL YOU'RE DOING, BUT... WELL, TAKE CARE OF YOURSELVES

WE'LL REMEMBER — AND *YOU'D* BETTER START FORGETTING NOW

MODESTY BLAISE
by PETER O'DONNELL

A burning sun rises over the South Atlantic

BLIMEY, I FEEL DEAD SOPPY SITTING 'ERE LIKE THIS, PRINCESS

IT'LL PASS WHEN THINGS GET STARTED, WILLIE...

...LET'S HAVE A FINAL RUN-THROUGH OF THE INFO ON DE SÁ

YOU RECKON THIS CAPER'LL HOT UP, THEN? THAT KOSSUTH *IS* ABOARD THE YACHT?

THAT'S THE C.I.A. HUNCH... AND WE USUALLY FOUND THOSE BOYS WERE GOOD GUESSERS IN THE DAYS WHEN *WE* WERE MARKETING INTELLIGENCE

139

MODESTY BLAISE
by PETER O'DONNELL

SO DE SÁ'S GOT A CREW OF FOURTEEN PLUS STEWARDS, AN' SIX OR SEVEN GUESTS

HANGERS-ON, IT SEEMS... I GUESS WE KNOW THE TYPE, WILLIE

THE PLAYBOYS AND PLAYGIRLS WHO LIVE EASY BY TRADING THEIR GAY COMPANY IN RETURN FOR BED AND BOARD

M'MM... AND 'OW DO *WE* STRIKE 'EM, PRINCESS? DOMESTIC BLISS OR CAT AN' DOG?

JUST WELL SUITED, I THINK ... ...OH, YOU'LL HAVE TO DITCH YOUR PRINCIPLES AND STOP DROPPING AITCHES, OR WE MIGHT SEEM ILL-ASSORTED, WILLIE LOVE

TALK ABOUT STOP AT *NOTHING!*

140

MODESTY BLAISE
by PETER O'DONNELL

Noon, aboard the Flamenco

BRIDGE TO SENOR DE SÁ — SMOKE FLARE OFF THE STARBOARD BOW... ABOUT TEN KILOMETRES

141

FLOATING OBJECT... A RUBBER DINGHY... THERE IS MOVEMENT ABOARD

COME ROUND ON COURSE FOR IT, CASADO

MODESTY BLAISE
by PETER O'DONNELL

MODESTY BLAISE
by PETER O'DONNELL

MODESTY BLAISE
by PETER O'DONNELL

MODESTY BLAISE
by PETER O'DONNELL

MODESTY BLAISE
by PETER O'DONNELL

YOU'VE REALLY HAD US *FORCED* ON YOU ALL THE WAY TO FREETOWN, SENOR DE SÃ—

JUST DE SÃ, MY DEAR... WE SHALL CALL YOU MOLLY, AND WE ARE HAPPY TO HAVE YOU

MY HUSBAND'S *LONGING* TO SEE OVER YOUR BEAUTIFUL SHIP—HE'S QUITE OVERWHELMED BY IT

TOMORROW WE WILL MAKE A TOUR...

BUT MEANWHILE, LET US DRINK TO... WHAT SHALL IT BE? TO BEING OVERWHELMED PERHAPS?

ER-YES, I SUPPOSE SO... THIS IS CERTAINLY A BIG EXPERIENCE FOR US

MODESTY BLAISE
by PETER O'DONNELL

A NEW DAY... AND *THE FLAMENCO* SAILS ON WITH ITS UNEXPECTED GUESTS

AH, I SEE— AND WHAT'S THE CRUISING RADIUS?

SIX THOUSAND MILES, SENOR...

THE DIESELS RUN AT 230 R.P.M. AND GIVE A TOTAL OF NEARLY TWO THOUSAND HORSE-POWER

LET'S LEAVE YOUR HUSBAND TO ENJOY THESE TECHNICAL MATTERS— WOULD YOU LIKE TO SEE THE OWNER'S SUITE?

OH— *YOUR* SUITE? YES, I'D LOVE TO

MODESTY BLAISE
by PETER O'DONNELL

*F*OUR DAYS SINCE "MR. AND MRS. CHEYNEY" WERE PICKED UP— AND FREETOWN NOW LIES ONLY TWELVE HOURS AWAY...

BILL! IF YOU CAN SPARE ME A MINUTE...?

OH— ER, YES, OF COURSE, DARLING

THERE WILL NOW BE A DOMESTIC TIFF IN THE CABIN, I THINK— MR. CHEYNEY HAS A WANDERING EYE, KAVERIN

ELUSIVE, I FEAR... AT ONE TIME SHE SEEMED *VERY* PROMISING, BUT—

PERHAPS SHE DECIDED YOU ARE NOT THE TYPE TO LET SLIP SECRETS IN THE BOUDOIR, DE SÃ...

AND... MRS. CHEYNEY?

MODESTY BLAISE
by PETER O'DONNELL

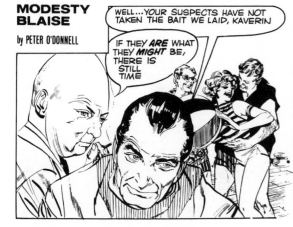

WELL... YOUR SUSPECTS HAVE NOT TAKEN THE BAIT WE LAID, KAVERIN

IF THEY *ARE* WHAT THEY *MIGHT* BE, THERE IS STILL TIME

*I*N MODESTY AND WILLIE'S CABIN...

WE'VE CHECKED EVERY INCH OF THE SHIP— 'CEPT *ONE* PLACE WE HAVEN'T BEEN ABLE TO GET AT EASY

I KNOW... AND IF KOSSUTH'S ABOARD, THAT'S WHERE HE'S GOT TO BE

I DON'T *LIKE* IT SOMEHOW, PRINCESS — MAKES MY EARS PRICKLE

CAN'T BE HELPED, WILLIE LOVE... STICKING OUR NECKS OUT IS WHAT WE'RE HERE FOR

MODESTY BLAISE
by PETER O'DONNELL

IT FIGURES, WILLIE—THAT SMALL CABIN ON THE LOWER-DECK IS THE ONLY PLACE ON THE SHIP THAT'S ALWAYS KEPT *LOCKED*

GOING TO BE DODGY, CHECKING IF KOSSUTH'S IN THERE

THAT'S WHY WE'VE COVERED EVERY OTHER ANGLE FIRST

OKAY... TONIGHT, THEN?

IT'LL HAVE TO BE—WE REACH FREETOWN BEFORE DAWN, AND WE'VE GOT TO *KNOW* WHETHER KOSSUTH IS ABOARD BEFORE WE GET OFF

154

MODESTY BLAISE
by PETER O'DONNELL

*A*N HOUR AFTER MIDNIGHT...

SURE YOU WON'T NEED ME, WILLIE?

SAFER ON ME OWN, PRINCESS— I'LL BE BACK IN TEN MINUTES... AND IF I'M CAUGHT PROWLING, I'M AN ERRANT HUSBAND GOIN' TO MARGARITA

SUPPOSE I DO FIND KOSSUTH— ANY ACTION?

NONE— WE JUST REPORT TO SIR GERALD'S MAN IN FREETOWN, AND THE AMERICAN NAVY WILL TAKE IT FROM THERE

YEAH... SEEMS ALMOST TOO DULL TO BE TRUE, I RECKON

155

MODESTY BLAISE
by PETER O'DONNELL

*W*ILLIE GARVIN MOVES LIKE A SHADOW THROUGH THE SLEEPING SHIP....

IF KOSSUTH'S HERE, LET'S 'OPE THEY'VE GOT HIM UNDER SEDATION, LIKE THE PRINCESS RECKONS— DON'T WANT 'IM TO START CREATING...

THE PICKLOCK PROBES...AND TURNS

156

MODESTY BLAISE
by PETER O'DONNELL

*I*N THE SMALL CABIN WHICH IS ALWAYS KEPT LOCKED...

AHH— WE'VE 'IT THE JACKPOT! THAT'S *GOTTER* BE DR. KOSSUTH...

WHY, MR. CHEYNEY! ARE YOU LOOKING FOR SOMETHING?

KAVERIN! BUT IT'S NOT HIS CABIN!

I-I'M ON THE WRONG *DECK!* THOUGHT THIS WAS MARGARITA'S CABIN! BEEN DRINKING, WAITING FOR MY WIFE TO GO TO SLEEP— OH, MY GOD, DON'T MENTION THIS TO *HER!*

157

MODESTY BLAISE by PETER O'DONNELL

ALL RIGHT, WILLIE, I— I'M AWAKE NOW... FILL ME IN

THEY MUST'VE FIGURED WE COULD BE PHONIES, SO THEY SET UP THAT LOCKED CABIN AS A BAIT

I FOUND KAVERIN THERE! AN' NEXT MINUTE SOMEONE CHILLED ME WITH A COSH FROM BEHIND

NO SIGN OF KOSSUTH?

NONE! LOOK, YOU'D BETTER GET DRIED OFF, PRINCESS... DE SA MIGHT LOOK IN AGAIN SOON, AND WE'RE S'POSED TO BE SHACKLED

MODESTY BLAISE by PETER O'DONNELL

WILLIE TAKES OUT THE LOOSENED SCREWS OF THE VENTILATOR-COVER...

HOW'D THEY GET *YOU*, THEN?

GIFT-WRAPPED ON A VELVET CUSHION ... I STARTED *WORRYING* WHEN YOU DIDN'T COME BACK AFTER HALF AN HOUR...

SO I GOT DRESSED AND WENT TO THAT CABIN, *LOOKING* FOR YOU... THEY WERE WAITING, OF COURSE... GUN IN MY NECK AND A NEEDLE IN MY ARM

SORRY, WILLIE LOVE— IT WASN'T SMART

IT WAS NICE THOUGH, PRINCESS... LET'S NOT GET TOO SMART TO WORRY ABOUT EACH OTHER, EH?

MODESTY BLAISE by PETER O'DONNELL

OKAY?

FINE

GOOD THING WE HID THE TOOLS SOON AS WE GOT ABOARD

IF THE CREW'S BEHIND DE SA, WE'LL HAVE A DOZEN MEN AGAINST US, WILLIE... MUCH TOO MANY

HOSTAGE PLAY? GRAB DE SA AND—

NO, IT'S THE WRONG SCHOOL FOR THAT GAME... JUST MAKE LIKE WE'RE HANDCUFFED AGAIN, WILLIE, AND TELL ME—*WHERE THE HELL IS KOSSUTH?*

MODESTY BLAISE by PETER O'DONNELL

OUR DR. KOSSUTH *HAD* TO BE IN THAT LOCKED CABIN... BUT HE WASN'T! SO IF HE'S NOT ABOARD, WHY HAVE THEY NAILED US? AND IF HE IS — THEN *WHERE*?

LOOKS LIKE WE'VE MISSED A TRICK SOMEWHERE...

BUT WE'RE NOT THE ONLY ONES! GENUINE OLD REGULATION 'CUFFS — I *ASK* YOU!

A KEY TURNS IN THE DOOR...

NO ACTION YET, WILLIE— WE'RE DOPEY AND WE'RE BEAT!

MODESTY BLAISE
by PETER O'DONNELL

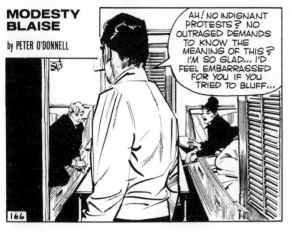

AH! NO INDIGNANT PROTESTS? NO OUTRAGED DEMANDS TO KNOW THE MEANING OF THIS? I'M SO GLAD... I'D FEEL EMBARRASSED FOR YOU IF YOU TRIED TO BLUFF...

WHAT... HAPPENS NOW?

WELL, I WAS FOR KILLING YOU RIGHT AWAY— BUT THAT DREARY MAN KAVERIN INSISTS ON GETTING SANCTION FROM HIS—AH— SUPERIORS

HE'S SENT A MESSAGE—WHICH MUST GO THROUGH *TWO* RELAY SHIPS, IF YOU PLEASE! THERE WILL BE A REPLY SOME TIME TONIGHT, BUT... IT WON'T AFFECT *MY* DECISION

166

MODESTY BLAISE
by PETER O'DONNELL

I'M SORRY YOU HAVE TO BE PUT DOWN, ESPECIALLY *YOU*, MY DEAR — BUT I SHALL DO IT, WHATEVER KAVERIN'S SUPERIORS SAY

YOUR... YOUR CREW WON'T—

THEY'RE ALL HANDPICKED, AND THEY KNOW THIS TRIP WILL PAY ME *ONE MILLION DOLLARS*, ENOUGH TO SAVE THE DE SA EMPIRE... AND THEY ARE *PART* OF THAT EMPIRE

A MILLION..? SO YOU *HAVE* GOT KOSSUTH ABOARD?

IT'S HARDLY WORTH YOUR WHILE TO WORRY ABOUT THAT QUESTION NOW, I'M AFRAID

167

MODESTY BLAISE
by PETER O'DONNELL

LISTEN, DE SA— WE CAN GET YOU *MORE* THAN A MILLION DOLLARS FOR KOSSUTH

YOU'RE ASSUMING I'VE GOT HIM, AREN'T YOU?

AND IF I HAD, I'M BOUND TO REMEMBER THAT KAVERIN'S SERVICE PRACTISES VENGEANCE— UNLIKE YOUR WESTERN INTELLIGENCE SERVICES...

BESIDES, I'M AN *HONEST* MAN—WHEN I'M BOUGHT, I *STAY* BOUGHT

168

MODESTY BLAISE
by PETER O'DONNELL

WELL... WHAT'S OUR CAPER NOW, PRINCESS?

GETTING OUT ALIVE, WILLIE— BUT WE CAN'T WIN IN A STAND-UP FIGHT

WE'LL WAIT TILL HALFWAY THROUGH THE MIDDLE WATCH... THERE'LL ONLY BE ONE OFFICER AND THE HELMSMAN ON THE BRIDGE ...NAIL THEM, AND RUN THE SHIP AGROUND

I GUESS WE'LL BE SOMEWHERE NORTH OF CONAKRY... SANDY COAST BACKED BY MANGROVE FOREST... THINK YOU CAN COPE, WILLIE LOVE?

I WAS WITH THE FOREIGN LEGION PARAS IN THE JUNGLE AROUND DIEN BIEN PHU— YOU EITHER COPED OR CROAKED

169

MODESTY BLAISE
by PETER O'DONNELL

ON THE BRIDGE OF THE FLAMENCO... A HELMSMAN AND THE OFFICER OF THE WATCH

GIVE ME TWO MINUTES TO REACH THE STARBOARD LADDER, WILLIE— THEN WHOEVER'S NEARER THE *OFFICER* TAKES HIM *FIRST*...

THE HELMSMAN SHOULD HAVE HIS EYES DOWN, WATCHING THE COMPASS —SO THE OTHER ONE TAKES *HIM* ...OKAY?

CHECK

MODESTY BLAISE
by PETER O'DONNELL

THE KONGO, OR YAWARA STICK...JUST A SMALL WOODEN DUMB-BELL ...BUT A POWERFUL WEAPON WHEN USED BY A SKILLED HAND TO STRIKE AT THE NERVE– CENTRES OF THE BODY

THE OFFICER'S NEARER MODESTY'S SIDE...WAIT FOR HER TO TAKE 'IM...

AS MODESTY MOVES, THE MAN TURNS...

MODESTY BLAISE
by PETER O'DONNELL

MODESTY JABS WITH THE KONGO...AND THE ARM REACHING TOWARDS THE ALARM IS PARALYZED...

AN INSTANT LATER, THE KONGO HAMMERS HOME ON A NERVE– CENTRE FOR THE KNOCKOUT

CHECK AROUND, PRINCESS— I'LL TAKE THE WHEEL

MODESTY BLAISE
by PETER O'DONNELL

ALL CLEAR, PRINCESS?

YES, EVERYBODY'S ASLEEP—THERE'S NOBODY ON DECK OR IN THE CHART- ROOM

I'LL TAKE HER NOW—YOU BRING KOSSUTH UP TO THE PORT GANGWAY AND GET IT LOWERED, WILLIE...BETTER GAG HIM IF HE LOOKS LIKE WAKING UP

MODESTY SPINS THE WHEEL, AND THE FLAMENCO COMES SMOOTHLY ROUND... HEADING STRAIGHT FOR THE WILD COAST OF GUINEA

MODESTY BLAISE
by PETER O'DONNELL

ALL SET, PRINCESS — AN' KOSSUTH'S STILL OUT COLD

RIGHT... WE'LL BE HITTING THE BEACH IN ABOUT THREE MINUTES

RING 'FULL AHEAD' FOR ME, WILLIE LOVE, WE'VE GOT TO PLOUGH WELL INTO THE SHALLOWS — THEN TAKE KOSSUTH DOWN THE GANGWAY AND HANG ON TIGHT

THE FLAMENCO WEAVES BETWEEN SMALL, SWAMPY ISLANDS... THEN, QUIVERING AS THE KEEL CUTS INTO SOFT SAND, SHE THRUSTS ON

178

MODESTY BLAISE
by PETER O'DONNELL

A LONG JUDDER SHAKES *THE FLAMENCO* AS SHE SLOWS TO A HALT, HARD AGROUND

179

WHAT THE DEVIL—?

BRIDGE! ANSWER, DAMN YOU!

KEEP GOING WHEN YOU HIT THE BEACH, WILLIE— STRAIGHT INTO THE FOREST! I'LL COVER YOU

MODESTY BLAISE
by PETER O'DONNELL

C HAOS ABOARD THE *FLAMENCO*...

DE SÁ! WHAT—?

WE'RE AGROUND! IT'S THOSE TWO—!

GOMEZ! GET ON THE SEARCHLIGHT! CASADO! I WANT THE WHOLE CREW ON DECK— EVERY MAN WITH A GUN!

KOSSUTH, REVIVING, BEGINS TO STRUGGLE

NO! PLEASE — YOU DON'T UNDERSTAND!

THAT'S LIFE, MATEY. NOW BELT UP!

180

MODESTY BLAISE
by PETER O'DONNELL

K OSSUTH STRUGGLES WILDLY

I'LL 'AVE TO CHILL 'IM AGAIN, PRINCESS

NO— I'LL TAKE HIM, IT'S QUICKER

THEY'LL HAVE THAT SEARCHLIGHT GOING ANY MOMENT NOW,

THE KONGO, GRIPPED HARD AGAINST A NERVE IN THE WRIST, GIVES COMPLETE CONTROL

RIGHT! THIS WON'T HURT TOO MUCH SO LONG AS YOU DON'T FIGHT IT, DOCTOR... NOW, RUN, DAMN YOU!

181

MODESTY BLAISE
by PETER O'DONNELL

THE SEARCHLIGHT STABS OUT AND MOVES SLOWLY ACROSS THE BEACH . . .

THERE! HOLD IT!

TOO LATE, DE SÁ — THEY HAVE REACHED COVER

THEY WON'T MOVE FAR BY NIGHT... I'LL HAVE A PARTY OUT BY FIRST LIGHT

CASADO! HAVE AN ANCHOR DROPPED WELL ASTERN BY ONE OF THE LIFE-BOATS, AND START KEDGING THE SHIP OFF

IT MAY BE A BIG TASK, SENOR—WE ARE VERY HARD AGROUND IN THIS SAND

182

MODESTY BLAISE
by PETER O'DONNELL

IN THE COVER OF THE JUNGLE...

THIS IS YOUR KIND OF TERRAIN, WILLIE— SO YOU'RE THE BIG WHEEL

WE'LL MOVE INLAND HALF-A-MILE, THEN SETTLE DOWN FOR THE NIGHT

YOU CAN RECKON WE'RE OVER THE 'UMP NOW, PRINCESS... THEY'D NEED NATIVE TRACKERS TO PICK US UP IN THIS LOT

PLEASE...

ALL RIGHT, MATEY, I'LL TAKE YOU IN TANDEM NOW— I BROUGHT THE 'CUFFS ALONG

183

MODESTY BLAISE
by PETER O'DONNELL

WON'T BE A *COMFY* TRIP TO CONAKRY, PRINCESS, BUT WE'LL MAKE OUT...THERE'S FRUIT, NUTS, SMALL GAME, AN' A LOT OF RIVERS

YOU *MUST* LET ME GO! I—I *KNOW* YOU'RE TRYING TO HELP, BUT—

WE *WERE,* KOSSUTH...WE THOUGHT YOU'D BEEN KIDNAPPED, AND WE CAME TO GET YOU BACK

NOW WE FIND YOU'VE RATTED... BUT WE'RE TAKING YOU BACK JUST THE SAME— YOU'RE A VERY IMPORTANT PROPERTY

184

MODESTY BLAISE
by PETER O'DONNELL

IN A ROCKY HOLLOW...

SAFE ENOUGH TO 'AVE A LITTLE FIRE SMOULDERING, IT'LL HELP KEEP THE RUDDY INSECTS OFF

'AS OUR V.I.P. SAID ANYTHING YET, PRINCESS?

WHAT *CAN* HE SAY...?

SUCH A CAPABLE YOUNG WOMAN...AND SO ARROGANT...READY TO JUDGE WITHOUT KNOWLEDGE

YOU WERE A REFUGEE, KOSSUTH— THAT MADE YOU A GOOD CAUSE IN MY BOOK...

BUT NOW YOU'RE RUNNING *BACK* TO THE PEOPLE YOU SPENT HALF YOUR LIFE RUNNING *AWAY* FROM— AND I HATE A MASOCHIST

A SUBTLE DIAGNOSIS, YOUNG WOMAN... BUT WRONG

185

MODESTY BLAISE by PETER O'DONNELL

ON THE FLAMENCO

IF I CAN'T HAVE KOSSUTH ALIVE, I WANT HIM *DEAD*, DE SA — AND THE PRICE WILL BE REDUCED ACCORDINGLY

I'LL GET HIM BACK ALIVE...

...TO MOVE SOUTH, THEY MUST GO UP-RIVER TO FIND A PLACE TO CROSS. I'LL TAKE A PARTY UP BY BOAT TO CATCH THEM

IN THE JUNGLE...

GOOD... LET'S HAVE ONE ALL ROUND WHILE DR. KOSSUTH EXPOUNDS ON WHAT MAKES HIM TICK

I RECKON THESE FAGS 'AVE DRIED OUT ENOUGH NOW, PRINCESS

MODESTY BLAISE by PETER O'DONNELL

I WILL TELL YOU WHY I AGREED TO GO BACK TO HUNGARY... YOU WILL DESPISE MY SENSE OF VALUES, OF COURSE, BUT I AM NOT ASHAMED

I GO BACK FOR ONE REASON ONLY— BECAUSE THEY HAVE MY CHILD THERE

YOUR *CHILD?* BUT YOU WERE NEVER MARRIED!

YOUNG WOMAN... I DO ASSURE YOU THAT MARRIAGE IS NOT *ALWAYS* A CONDITION PRECEDENT OF FATHERHOOD...

MODESTY BLAISE by PETER O'DONNELL

WE WERE IN LOVE, AND WE PLANNED TO MARRY... BUT THEN CAME THE REVOLT IN HUNGARY, AND I WAS AMONG THE THOUSANDS WHO ESCAPED

BUT NOT THE WOMAN?

NO... ANNA HAD GONE TO HER HOME IN MISKOLC... I THOUGHT SHE WOULD FOLLOW ME, BUT THE RISING WAS CRUSHED TOO QUICKLY

I GIVE YOU THE TRUTH — I LOVED MY FREEDOM MORE THAN I LOVED ANNA ...BUT IF I HAD KNOWN SHE WAS TO BEAR MY CHILD, I WOULD HAVE STAYED...

MODESTY BLAISE by PETER O'DONNELL

MY DAUGHTER IS SIX YEARS OLD NOW... AND ANNA, HER MOTHER, DIED WHEN SHE WAS BORN

WHEN DID YOU LEARN ALL THIS?

ONLY WHEN DE SA MADE CONTACT WITH ME IN RIO DE JANEIRO... SHOWED ME DOCUMENTS, PHOTOGRAPHS, RECORDS... A LETTER FROM ANNA'S SISTER CONFIRMED BY A SPANISH DIPLOMAT WHOM I TRUST COMPLETELY

OH, THE PROOF IS POSITIVE ENOUGH... I WOULD DOUBT IT IF I COULD, BELIEVE ME

STREWTH, THIS'LL RIP THE PRINCESS APART...

MODESTY BLAISE
by PETER O'DONNELL

SO I HAVE NEVER SEEN THIS CHILD OF MINE... BUT HER SAFETY AND HAPPINESS MEAN MORE TO ME THAN POWER-GROUPS OR MILITARY SECRETS... *THAT* IS WHY I WAS GOING BACK

WHERE IS SHE NOW?

IT IS POLITE OF YOU TO ASK... BUT I HARDLY THINK *YOU* CAN IMAGINE WHAT IT IS TO BE A SMALL GIRL, QUITE ALONE, IN A PRISON CAMP—

190

I DON'T HAVE TO IMAGINE— I KNOW, DAMN YOU!

SURE, PRINCESS... EASY NOW

MODESTY BLAISE
by PETER O'DONNELL

STRANGE... I DID NOT THINK THAT YOUNG WOMAN COULD BE MOVED BY THE PLIGHT OF A SMALL CHILD

NO?... REMEMBER THE PRISON-CAMP AT KALYROS? YOU WERE THERE TWENTY YEARS BACK...

WHAT D'YOU RECKON *THAT* WAS LIKE FOR A SIX-YEAR-OLD GIRL... ON 'ER OWN?

KALYROS? MY GOD, IT WAS LIKE A CORNER OF HELL... BUT I RECALL NO CHILDREN, THEY COULD NOT HAVE SURVIVED IT

THERE'S ONE WHO DID, MATEY... AN' HALF-A-DOZEN REFUGEE AN' D.P. CAMPS AFTER THAT... *YOU'VE LIFTED THE LID ON EVERYTHING* THAT HAPPENED TO HER IN THOSE YEARS

191

MODESTY BLAISE
by PETER O'DONNELL

YOUNG WOMAN... I OWE YOU AN APOLOGY... YOUR FRIEND HAS TOLD ME SOMETHING OF YOUR CHILDHOOD

IT'S LONG PAST NOW... I DON'T REMEMBER MY PARENTS... BUT I USED TO DREAM THAT THEY'D COME FOR ME ONE DAY

I EXPECT YOUR DAUGHTER HAS THE SAME DREAM

I WANT TO MAKE THAT DREAM COME TRUE... YOU WANT TO PREVENT IT, AND FOR GOOD REASON

WE ARE BOTH TRYING TO DO WHAT WE MUST... BUT AT LEAST WE HAVE UNDERSTANDING FOR EACH OTHER AND NOT ENMITY

YES

192

MODESTY BLAISE
by PETER O'DONNELL

IN THE CAMP AT KALYROS, HUMAN BEINGS FOUGHT LIKE ANIMALS OVER A SCRAP OF ROTTING OFFAL... AND SHE WAS *ALONE* THERE.....A CHILD!

SHE'S NOT FEELING SORRY FOR *HERSELF*, Y'KNOW... SHE NEVER *HAS*.

NO... BUT SHE CAN HAVE LITTLE SORROW TO SPARE FOR MY OWN CHILD, I WOULD THINK

HOUR TO DAWN, PRINCESS— TIME WE MOVED

RIGHT, WILLIE

IN MODESTY'S HAND— THE DEADLY LITTLE KONGO

193

MODESTY BLAISE
by PETER O'DONNELL

MODESTY BLAISE
by PETER O'DONNELL

MODESTY BLAISE
by PETER O'DONNELL

MODESTY BLAISE
by PETER O'DONNELL

MODESTY BLAISE
by PETER O'DONNELL

FUNNY... I THOUGHT YOU MIGHT LET KOSSUTH GO— BUT I DIDN'T RECKON ON THE KNOCK-OUT BIT

I WOULDN'T BLAME YOU FOR WALKING OUT ON ME, WILLIE...

BUT IF I HAVE A CHOICE, I'D RATHER YOU BEAT ME STUPID AND CALLED IT QUITS

YOU ONLY DID IT SO I WOULDN'T CARRY THE CAN WITH YOU, PRINCESS... I JUST WISH I'D THOUGHT OF IT FIRST, THAT'S ALL

198

MODESTY BLAISE
by PETER O'DONNELL

IT NOT GOING TO BE A MILK-RUN GETTING TO CONAKRY, PRINCESS... WE'LL EAT OKAY, AND MOST OF THE BIG GAME'S FURTHER INLAND...

BUT THERE'S CROCS— AN' WE'VE GOT A LOT OF RIVERS TO CROSS

THE BIGGEST RIVER I'VE GOT TO CROSS IS TELLING SIR GERALD WHAT I'VE DONE, WILLIE...

199

MODESTY BLAISE
by PETER O'DONNELL

LONDON... AFTER THREE GRUELING WEEKS THROUGH THE JUNGLE TO CONAKRY, A BOAT TO FREETOWN, AND AN AIR-PASSAGE HOME

FRASER? MODESTY BLAISE

I'VE JUST GOT IN— CAN I SEE SIR GERALD IF I COME ROUND IN ABOUT AN HOUR?

THE BRIEF REPORT YOU SENT ON BY COURIER GAVE THE *FACTS*, MISS BLAISE— ANY *EXPLANATION* SEEMS IMPOSSIBLE

OF COURSE... BUT HE'S ENTITLED TO SAY HIS PIECE TO ME, FRASER— TELL HIM I'LL BE ALONE, WILLIE GARVIN DISAPPEARED AT LONDON AIRPORT

200

MODESTY BLAISE
by PETER O'DONNELL

YOU KNEW DOCTOR KOSSUTH'S IMPORTANCE TO THE WEST... YOU FOUND HE WAS A DEFECTOR, NOT A KIDNAP-VICTIM... *AND YOU LET HIM GO!*

I CAN'T *DEMAND* AN EXPLANATION— YOUR WORK FOR ME IS QUITE UNOFFICIAL—

MY REASONS WOULDN'T IMPRESS YOU AT ALL, SIR GERALD

201

THEY MADE SENSE TO WILLIE GARVIN... HE WAS HERE HALF AN HOUR AGO, EXPLAINING ON YOUR BEHALF WITH GREAT BELLIGERENCE

WILLIE!... SO THAT'S WHY HE FADED OUT AT THE AIRPORT

MODESTY BLAISE by PETER O'DONNELL

YOU KNOW WILLIE GARVIN HAD NO PART IN WHAT I DID?

I KNOW YOU DIDN'T *ALLOW* HIM A PART — YOU KNOCKED HIM OUT

CONFOUND IT, MODESTY! I JUST CAN'T SEE *YOU* OF ALL PEOPLE ACTING ON AN EMOTIONAL IMPULSE!

I DIDN'T... I THOUGHT IT THROUGH FROM ALL SIDES

YOUR SIDE, KOSSUTH'S, THE AMERICANS', THE WESTERN ALLIANCE... AND THE ONE SIDE *I* KNOW BETTER THAN ANY OF YOU— *Kossuth's child, the little girl's side*

202

MODESTY BLAISE by PETER O'DONNELL

YOU RATED THE LIFE OF ONE CHILD MORE IMPORTANT THAN KEEPING A SCIENTIFIC GENIUS FOR THE WEST?

THAT WAS EASY

203

...I DON'T GIVE A DAMN ABOUT A SCIENTIST GOING ONE WAY OR THE OTHER, SIR GERALD — IT'S NOTHING NEW, AND IT NEVER SEEMS TO MAKE MUCH DIFFERENCE IN THE LONG RUN

FOR ME, WHAT TWISTED THE THUMBSCREWS WAS CHOOSING WHETHER TO FAIL *YOU* OR FAIL THE CHILD

YE-E-ES... WITH YOUR BACKGROUND, ABOUT THE ONLY DEAL IN THE PACK I COULD LOSE

MODESTY BLAISE by PETER O'DONNELL

I REALIZE YOU WON'T WANT ME TO WORK FOR YOU AGAIN... I GUESS AMERICAN INTELLIGENCE IS HOPPING MAD, TOO

NO... IT WAS A LONG-SHOT AND THEY EXPECTED FAILURE

SO THEY'RE WELL-PLEASED WITH SECOND BEST— IN FACT I'VE A GLOWING MESSAGE OF THANKS TO PASS ON TO YOU

WHAT DO YOU MEAN— *SECOND BEST?*

I MEAN THAT THOUGH KOSSUTH CAN'T WORK FOR THE WEST, HE CAN'T WORK FOR THE EAST EITHER... HE'S DEAD, MODESTY

204

MODESTY BLAISE by PETER O'DONNELL

KOSSUTH— *DEAD?* HOW?

LET'S TAKE IT FROM WHEN YOU AND WILLIE DIDN'T COME OFF DE SA'S YACHT AT FREETOWN— THAT MADE US THINK, RATHER

THEN THE AMERICAN TRACKING PLANE SAW THE YACHT BEACHED... IT LOOKED VERY MUCH LIKE YOUR HANDWRITING

IN SIX HOURS A U.S. NAVY DESTROYER WAS THERE, DOING A FRIENDS-IN-NEED ACT— MEN SWARMING OVER THE BEACH AND YACHT— SHORT OF VIOLENCE, DE SA COULDN'T STOP THEM

205

MODESTY BLAISE
by PETER O'DONNELL

MODESTY BLAISE
by PETER O'DONNELL

Modesty BLAISE
THE GABRIEL SET-UP
by PETER O'DONNELL and JIM HOLDAWAY

MODESTY BLAISE
by PETER O'DONNELL

MODESTY BLAISE
by PETER O'DONNELL

MODESTY BLAISE
by PETER O'DONNELL

WHERE'S GABRIEL NOW?

"LAKESIDE". BIG HOUSE HALF-AN-HOUR'S DRIVE WEST, AND FOUR MILES OFF THE HIGHWAY—HE'S GOT A BUNCH OF HIS TOP EXECS THERE, FROM ALL OVER

HE'LL BE HERE TOMORROW, AND HE'LL WANT TO CHECK EVERY DEPARTMENT...

...BUT ESPECIALLY HE'LL WANT TO SEE US HANDLE A *Cloud Nine* OPERATION

ONLY ONE IN SIX YIELD PAY-DIRT—BUT I'LL HAVE A LIKELY PATIENT ON THE TABLE FOR HIM

MODESTY BLAISE
by PETER O'DONNELL

YOU WANT ME TO TELL THE STAFF ABOUT GABRIEL COMING TO MAKE A CHECK-UP?

YES... DO THAT

HELL, NOT THE MUG-STAFF! I JUST MEAN THE GUYS IN THE SET-UP!

RELAX, EDDIE... WOULD I GO AROUND TELLING ALL OUR DEVOTED MEDICS AND NURSES THAT THEY'RE FRONTING FOR A *RACKET?*

SURE... WELL, THE STORY FOR THEM IS THAT A DR. RUSKIN, AN OLD FRIEND OF MINE, IS PAYING US A VISIT

MODESTY BLAISE
by PETER O'DONNELL

IT'S YOUR VISITOR, SIR—

GABRIEL COMES TO THE PHOENIX SANATORIUM

AH, DR. RUSKIN! COME IN, COME IN! AND THANK YOU, SUSAN

WELL, WE CAN TALK NOW... I MUST SAY IT'S GREAT TO HAVE A VISIT FROM YOU

VARLEY... FIRST YOU TAKE ME ROUND, THEN YOU SHOW ME THE FILES, THEN YOU GIVE ME A VERBAL RUNDOWN ON EVERYTHING ...LET'S GO

MODESTY BLAISE
by PETER O'DONNELL

A TOUR OF THE PHOENIX SANATORIUM

PLENTY OF CUSTOMERS?

A WAITING LIST—WE DON'T TAKE ANYONE REALLY SICK OF COURSE, JUST RICH NEUROTICS, RUN-DOWN TYCOONS, OVERWORKED GOVERNMENT PEOPLE...

OUR STAFF IS GOOD, AND WE HAVE ALL THE MODERN TECHNIQUES—SO OUR REPUTATION'S GROWING, AS I SAID IN MY LAST REPORT

WE'RE GETTING PEOPLE FROM ACROSS THE BORDER, TOO! TWO PENTAGON MEN SO FAR, AND—

VARLEY... THAT'S WHY I SITED YOU HERE

MODESTY BLAISE
by PETER O'DONNELL

OH, DR. VARLEY! HAD MY *FIRST* SESSION IN *'Cloud Nine'* YESTERDAY, AND I JUST *HAVE* TO TELL YOU I FEEL A *NEW WOMAN*!

WE HAVE GREAT FAITH IN THAT TREATMENT, MRS. HASCOMBE

WITH THE DIRT SHE DISHED UP ON HERSELF IN *'Cloud Nine'* YOU CAN SQUEEZE HER FOR THE REST OF HER LIFE, GABRIEL

DON'T EVER START FIGURING WHAT I CAN DO WITH THE INFORMATION YOU GET FOR ME, VARLEY... COULD BE UNHEALTHY

SHOW ME *'Cloud Nine'*

219

MODESTY BLAISE
by PETER O'DONNELL

DOCTOR REEVE IS DUE TO RUN A *Cloud Nine* SESSION ABOUT NOW

ON?

ON A PATIENT WHO'S A TOP TECHNICIAN IN QUEBO PLASTICS... WE'LL WATCH FROM THE CONTROL-ROOM

JOHN HERE MAKES A FINE JOB OF THESE OPERATIONS

JOHN HERE IS PAID TO

220

MODESTY BLAISE
by PETER O'DONNELL

IN THE SOFTLY-LIT, SOUNDPROOF ROOM CALLED 'Cloud Nine'...

I'M TOLD THIS WEIRDIE TREATMENT OF YOURS IS A WHOLE LOT BETTER THAN TRANQUILLISER PILLS, DR. REEVE

NOTHING WEIRDIE ABOUT IT, MR. VALE— JUST A CAREFUL COMBINATION OF PROVEN *NATURAL* METHODS OF INDUCING RELAXATION! THE CEILING AQUARIUM FOR VISUAL...

...SOFT MUSIC FOR AURAL WARM-WATER BED FOR TACTILE, AND SO ON

IF THIS GUY'S A CHEMIST WITH QUEBO PLASTICS HE SHOULD HAVE PLENTY TO TELL...

221

MODESTY BLAISE
by PETER O'DONNELL

IN THE DIM, WARM LIGHT OF 'Cloud Nine', TO THE FAINT SOUND OF SLUMBROUS MUSIC, THE PATIENT WATCHES THE SLOW MOVEMENT OF TROPICAL FISH ABOVE

EVERYTHING JUST RIGHT?

FINE... BUT WON'T IT ALL BE WASTED IF I DOZE OFF?

IT WOULD— BUT YOU WON'T, MR. VALE! I'LL BE BACK IN TWO HOURS, AND IT'LL SEEM LIKE TEN MINUTES TO YOU... BUT YOU'LL STILL BE AWAKE, I PROMISE YOU

IN THE CONTROL ROOM...

HERE'S WHERE WE SWITCH IN THE SUBLIMINAL TAPES, GABRIEL —THE VISUAL AND THE AUDIO

222

MODESTY BLAISE
by PETER O'DONNELL

IN THE CONTROL ROOM, GABRIEL WATCHES A 'CLOUD NINE' SESSION THROUGH TO ITS CONCLUSION

OKAY, WE'RE OFF THE AIR

NICE DIGGING, JOHN—LOOKS LIKE YOU'VE GOT A RICH VEIN TO MINE THERE

WHEN THE TAPE'S TRANSCRIBED I'LL STUDY WHAT HE TOLD US, THEN RUN A FOLLOW-UP SESSION NEXT WEEK

WELL....! I HOPE YOU LIKED IT, GABRIEL!

I LIKED IT... NOW SHOW ME THE FILES

223

MODESTY BLAISE
by PETER O'DONNELL

IN THE OFFICE OF DR. VARLEY, HEAD OF THE PHOENIX SANATORIUM

WE SIMPLY CLASSIFY ALL INFORMATION WE GET UNDER FOUR HEADS, LIKE YOU SAID— INDUSTRIAL SECRETS, FINANCIAL SECRETS, INTELLIGENCE... AND DIRT

FIRST CATEGORY GIVES THE BIGGEST YIELD, BUT INTELLIGENCE IS BUILDING UP NICELY

A-F

EVERY COMPLETED FILE IS SENT TO YOUR MAN IN NEW YORK, AND THEN I IMAGINE HE GETS BUSY ON—

VARLEY... NONE OF MY PEOPLE IMAGINE WHAT THE OTHERS ARE BUSY ON... *EVER!*

224

MODESTY BLAISE
by PETER O'DONNELL

OH, I'M NOT INQUISITIVE... BUT I READ HOW SHARMAN CHEMICALS SPENT FOUR MILLION BUCKS DEVELOPING A NEW ANTI-BIOTIC...

...THEN FALSTEIN'S IN GERMANY CAME OUT WITH IT A MONTH AHEAD AND AT A QUARTER THE PRICE! MUST HAVE PAID A BOMB FOR THAT SECRET— AND IT'S ONE WE DUG OUT FOR YOU *HERE!*

VARLEY... DON'T FIGURE BEYOND YOUR JOB, OR YOU'RE *OUT*... AND WITH WHAT YOU KNOW, I WOULDN'T JUST *FIRE* YOU— YOU READ ME?

225

MODESTY BLAISE
by PETER O'DONNELL

GABRIEL FINISHES HIS INSPECTION OF THE PHOENIX SANATORIUM

226

HOW DID IT GO?

IT WENT FINE... SO I'M ONLY SWEATING... IF IT HADN'T, I'D BE SCARED SPITLESS

BUT I WISH LIKE HELL HE'D PICKED SOME PLACE OTHER THAN *'LAKESIDE'* TO HOLD A CONVENTION OF HIS TOP BRASS— IT'S TOO CLOSE

MODESTY BLAISE by PETER O'DONNELL

227

228

MODESTY BLAISE by PETER O'DONNELL

229

MODESTY BLAISE by PETER O'DONNELL

230

MODESTY BLAISE
by PETER O'DONNELL

WHEN WILLIE WRITES THAT THIS HAS ALL THE MARKS OF A *GABRIEL SET-UP*... WHAT DOES HE MEAN?

THAT *IF* IT'S A SET-UP, IT'S SOMETHING BIG, HIGHLY-ORGANISED ...AND BIZARRE

239

DOES 'GABRIEL' ACTUALLY EXIST? WE KNOW HIM ONLY AS A VAGUE PRESENCE, A WHISPERED NAME, CREDITED WITH BEING THE BRAINS BEHIND MAJOR CRIMINAL COUPS ALL OVER THE WORLD

GABRIEL EXISTS... I'VE MET HIM

CURIOSITY ALWAYS GIVES ME A CRAVING FOR OYSTERS— COME AND TELL ME ABOUT HIM OVER LUNCH, MODESTY

MODESTY BLAISE
by PETER O'DONNELL

TELL ME ABOUT GABRIEL

I ONLY MET HIM ONCE, FOR A FEW MINUTES... IT WAS IN '59, WHEN I WAS RUNNING *THE NETWORK*, AND WE WERE PLANNING TO LIFT A GOLD SHIPMENT AT BEIRUT...

240

ONE OF GABRIEL'S GROUPS WAS ON THE SAME JOB, AND WE CROSSED WIRES... GABRIEL SENT FOR ME AND TOLD ME TO PULL OUT

AND YOU DID?

CHEAPER THAN FIGHTING AND LOSING A GANG WAR, SIR GERALD... GABRIEL WAS TOO BIG, AND I RAN *THE NETWORK* STRICTLY FOR PROFIT

MODESTY BLAISE
by PETER O'DONNELL

*T*HE LADIES' ANNEXE OF RAND'S CLUB...

I NEED SOMEBODY TO LOOK AT *THE PHOENIX* FOR ME...TO FIND OUT WHETHER IT'S A SET-UP, AND IF SO, HOW IT WORKS

I HOPED I WOULDN'T HAVE TO ASK YOU THIS, MODESTY, BUT...

I'LL CABLE WILLIE GARVIN TO EXPECT ME IN WINNIPEG

241

ARE YOU SURE? YOU-AH-BACKED DOWN AGAINST GABRIEL ONCE BEFORE

I HAD OTHER THINGS TO ATTEND TO THEN...AND SO HAS GABRIEL NOW. IT GIVES ME SUFFICIENT EDGE, I THINK

MODESTY BLAISE
by PETER O'DONNELL

*A*T THE LUMINOR HOTEL, IN TREMONT, ONTARIO, THE HEIRESS TO TIMBER MILLIONS IS THROWING A TANTRUM...

I'D LIKE TO RUN YOU UNDER A GANG-SAW, WILLIE GARVIN!

YOU'RE A LOW-DOWN TWO-TIMING SKUNK!

NOW ISN'T THAT JUST WHAT I'VE ALWAYS TOLD YOU, MARJ?

242

MODESTY BLAISE
by PETER O'DONNELL

MODESTY BLAISE
by PETER O'DONNELL

WILLIE GARVIN PICKS MODESTY UP AT THE AIRPORT...

MODESTY BLAISE
by PETER O'DONNELL

AT THE LUMINOR HOTEL...

MODESTY BLAISE
by PETER O'DONNELL

MODESTY BLAISE
by PETER O'DONNELL

WHAT DOES *YOUR* SERVICE KNOW ABOUT GABRIEL, SAM?

NOTHING FIRM... THREE YEARS BACK SOMEONE SOLD THE OPPOSITION A PINPOINT MAP OF EVERY RADAR STATION ON THE ARCTIC D.E.W.—LINE

WE *THINK* THAT WAS GABRIEL... WE ALSO THINK THAT SOME GOOD STUFF *WE'VE* BOUGHT CAME FROM HIM—BUT HE NEVER DEALS DIRECT, SO WE DON'T KNOW

DOWN IN THE STATES, THE F.B.I. THINK HE'S GOT A FINGER IN THE *COSA NOSTRA* RACKETS—BUT WITH GABRIEL NOBODY *KNOWS* ANYTHING, IT'S ALL GUESSES

LET'S COME DOWN TO CASES NOW— *THE PHOENIX!*

251

MODESTY BLAISE
by PETER O'DONNELL

WE RAN A CHECK ON THE PHOENIX SANATORIUM A WHILE BACK, AT TARRANT'S REQUEST— AND IT SHOWED UP CLEAN

IT'S JUST A RITZY REST-HOME FOR FOLK WITH NERVOUS TROUBLES — EXPERT STAFF, LATEST EQUIPMENT AND METHODS, FINE RECORD OF SUCCESS— WITH THE DOUGH THEY MAKE, THEY DON'T *NEED* TO BE PHONEY !

FIND A SAFE DOCTOR TO RECOMMEND ME FOR TREATMENT, SAM... WHEN WILLIE AND TARRANT *BOTH* HAVE THE SAME HUNCH THAT'S WHERE I LAY MY BET

252

MODESTY BLAISE
by PETER O'DONNELL

*A*T THE PHOENIX SANATORIUM...

RIGHT, MISS LESTER, I'LL HAVE YOU SHOWN TO YOUR ROOM NOW

THERE'LL BE A MEDICAL AND PSYCHIATRICAL CHECK-UP THIS AFTERNOON... AND THEN WE'LL BE ABLE TO WORK OUT AN INDIVIDUAL PROGRAMME OF TREATMENT FOR YOU

THANK YOU, DR. VARLEY

IF YOU'RE LIKE MOST PEOPLE WHO COME HERE, YOU'LL HAVE A VARIETY OF PILLS IN THAT BAG, MISS LESTER— JUST GIVE THEM TO NURSE, PLEASE, WE DON'T LIKE THEM HERE

253

MODESTY BLAISE
by PETER O'DONNELL

IS THIS NEW PATIENT PROMISING?

NOT VERY... SHE'S FROM ENGLAND... HER FATHER MAKES JAM AND MILLIONS

Jane Lester

WE JUST MIGHT GET SOMETHING OUT OF HER FOR THE STOCK MARKET FILES, BUT I DOUBT IT

MORE LIKELY TO GET SOME SQUEEZE- DIRT ON HER...

I SAW HER IN THE CORRIDOR JUST NOW, AND I'D SAY SHE'S GOT SECRETS, THAT ONE

254

MODESTY BLAISE
by PETER O'DONNELL

THAT LOOKS RATHER FUN, DR. REEVE

IT'S THE CATHARSIS-CENTRE, WHERE A PATIENT CAN GET RID OF HIS AGGRESSIONS... BUT I DON'T THINK IT'S FOR YOU, MISS LESTER— OUR TESTS SHOW YOU AS VERY WELL-ADJUSTED

I... I DON'T *FEEL* THAT WAY

BORED AND IDLE... IF WE MIX PLENTY OF EXERCISE IN WITH THE TREATMENTS AND SLAP IN A KINGSIZED BILL, SHE'LL GO AWAY HAPPY...

255

MODESTY BLAISE
by PETER O'DONNELL

A NIGHT-CLUB IN TREMONT

WHERE'S MODESTY VANISHED TO, THIS LAST WEEK? YOU SAID YOU WERE WORKING ON SOME JOB *TOGETHER*, WILLIE

WELL THIS WAY SUITS *YOU*, DOESN'T IT, MARJ?

IT WOULD— IF I DIDN'T KNOW YOU'LL GO RUNNING THE MOMENT SHE *CROOKS* HER FINGER, YOU SMOOTH-TALKING RAT

'ALLO! SAM BARTH....!

TAKE FIVE, MARJ— I GOT TO SEE A BLOKE IN THE BAR

NOW *JUST* A MINUTE—!

256

MODESTY BLAISE
by PETER O'DONNELL

THE MANAGER, MARJ— I WANT TO GIVE 'IM AN EARFUL

WHO'S THIS 'BLOKE' YOU'VE SUDDENLY GOT TO SEE?

I WANT TO KNOW WHY THEY 'AVEN'T GOT A DOZEN RED ROSES 'ERE ON THE TABLE FOR YOU TONIGHT, LIKE I ORDERED

YOU DID? OH... WILLIE...!

GAW, I'M A *DIABOLICAL* LIAR...

257

MODESTY BLAISE
by PETER O'DONNELL

SOMETHING COME UP, SAM?

YEAH... THERE'S A BUNCH OF GUYS RENTED A BIG HOUSE WAY OFF THE HIGHWAY, ABOUT TWENTY MILES FROM THE PHOENIX

THEY'RE VISITORS, MOSTLY FOREIGN BUSINESSMEN.... PAPERS IN ORDER, EVERYTHING ON THE LEVEL

SO?

SO WE HAVE AN IDEA ONE OF THEM IS GABRIEL HIMSELF

258

MODESTY BLAISE
by PETER O'DONNELL

IN THE PHOENIX GYMNASIUM

ONLY ANOTHER FIVE MINUTES, MISS LESTER

DADDY'S NEVER GOING TO **BELIEVE** HOW HARD I'VE WORKED HERE—HE THINKS I'M LAZY

TEN MINUTES LATER

MY PROGRAMME OF TREATMENT HAS BEEN **VERY** EFFECTIVE, HONEY— I JUST WISH THEY WEREN'T SO **TERRIBLY** STRICT ABOUT THE **MEN** HERE

OH, WE MIX WITH THEM AT MEALS, AND IN FREE PERIODS

WHO WANTS TO **EAT** WITH THEM? SAY, HAVE YOU BEEN THROUGH 'CLOUD NINE' YET?

NO... BUT IT'S ON MY PROGRAMME FOR TOMORROW

MODESTY BLAISE
by PETER O'DONNELL

IN "Cloud Nine..."

MUSIC SUIT YOU, MISS LESTER? NOT TOO LOUD?

FINE, THANK YOU... AND THIS BED THING'S A DREAM! WHAT DO I HAVE TO DO?

JUST RELAX AND LEAVE IT TO 'CLOUD NINE'

AND THIS REALLY **DOES** SOMETHING FOR ME?

YOU'LL BE PLEASANTLY SURPRISED, MISS LESTER

OKAY... LET'S SWITCH IN THE SUBLIMINAL TAPES

MODESTY BLAISE
by PETER O'DONNELL

MODESTY BLAISE LIES IN THE QUIET SOLITUDE OF 'CLOUD NINE,' SOFT MUSIC IN HER EARS, WATCHING THE TROPICAL FISH DRIFTING SLOWLY IN THE AQUARIUM CEILING

BUT WITH THE MUSIC COMES A SUB-AUDIO VOICE, TOO QUIET FOR THE CONSCIOUS MIND TO REGISTER

YOU ARE COMFORTABLE... RELAXED... SLEEPY... NOTHING WILL DISTURB YOU...

Relax your body... you are growing sleepy... your eyes are closing...

AND EVERY FEW SECONDS SOMETHING FLICKERS ON THE GLASS CEILING ... FLICKERS AND IS GONE TOO SWIFTLY TO AROUSE AWARENESS

MODESTY BLAISE
by PETER O'DONNELL

AS THE UNHEARD VOICE SPEAKS, AND THE UNSEEN COMMANDS FLASH ON THE SCREEN ABOVE, MODESTY'S EYES CLOSE

Your body relaxed... your mind at rest

Sleep... Sleep

Deeper... deeper asleep

FIVE MINUTES... LOOKS LIKE SHE'S UNDER OKAY. I'LL TEST NOW

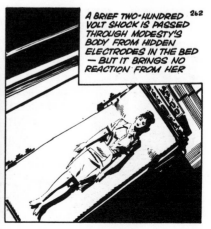

A BRIEF TWO-HUNDRED VOLT SHOCK IS PASSED THROUGH MODESTY'S BODY FROM HIDDEN ELECTRODES IN THE BED — BUT IT BRINGS NO REACTION FROM HER

MODESTY BLAISE by PETER O'DONNELL

MODESTY BLAISE LIES UNDER DEEP HYPNOSIS...WITHOUT EVER KNOWING THAT THE TECHNIQUE HAS BEEN APPLIED

CUTTING OUT THE SUBLIMINAL TAPES NOW

HERE'S WHERE WE GO ON TO DIRECT VOICE AT NORMAL VOLUME— I ALWAYS START WITH ROUTINE STUFF, TO ESTABLISH A PATTERN OF QUESTION— AND— ANSWER

263

MODESTY BLAISE by PETER O'DONNELL

YOU FEEL COMPLETELY RELAXED...YOU FEEL SAFE AND COMFORTABLE...

Jane Lester

THE VOICE MURMURS SOOTHINGLY IN MODESTY'S EAR

And you want to tell me all about yourself... you want to tell me everything

Now, what is your name?

I... DON'T KNOW...

264

MODESTY BLAISE by PETER O'DONNELL

THAT'S CRAZY! SHE *MUST* KNOW HER OWN NAME!

SHE SAYS NOT, AND SHE CAN'T TELL LIES UNDER DEEP HYPNOSIS! LET'S TRY IT ANOTHER WAY

IN THE Cloud Nine CONTROL ROOM...

Who are you?

I AM...

265

...MODESTY BLAISE

Jane Ingstan

SHE'S BOOKED IN AS *JANE LESTER!* THERE'S SOMETHING PHONEY HERE, JOHN!

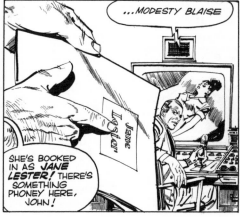

MODESTY BLAISE by PETER O'DONNELL

Why did you come here?

Were you sent by somebody?

Why are you using a false name?

Who sent you?

THE Cloud Nine SESSION CONTINUES... THE SOFT VOICE MURMURS URGENT, PROBING QUESTIONS

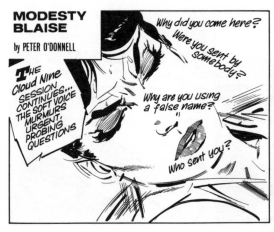

SHE'S NOT ANSWERING! YOU CAN'T HAVE GOT HER PROPERLY UNDER!

SHE'S UNDER DEEP HYPNOSIS OKAY... BUT HER SUBCONSCIOUS IS FIGHTING LIKE HELL TO KEEP ME OUT

THERE'S A DEFENCE-MECHANISM AT WORK THAT MUST HAVE BEEN BUILT-IN TO HER MIND A LONG TIME AGO

KEEP TRYING JOHN, AND LET ME KNOW IF SHE BREAKS— I'LL BE IN MY OFFICE

266

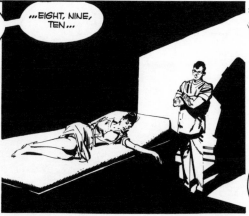

MODESTY BLAISE
by PETER O'DONNELL

271

MODESTY BLAISE
by PETER O'DONNELL

272

MODESTY BLAISE
by PETER O'DONNELL

273

MODESTY BLAISE
by PETER O'DONNELL

274

MODESTY BLAISE by PETER O'DONNELL

JUST RAN INTO AN OLD FRIEND, PRINCESS —

WE'LL SKIP THE CHAT

GABRIEL WANTS TO SEE YOU

WHERE, WHEN, AND WHAT ABOUT?

"LAKESIDE," TEN O'CLOCK TOMORROW MORNING, AND HE'LL TELL YOU WHAT ABOUT

ALL RIGHT, LERI... YOU CAN SAY WE'LL BE THERE

279

MODESTY BLAISE by PETER O'DONNELL

MORNING IN TREMONT

WILLIE, I—I DON'T WANT YOU TO GO WHEREVER IT IS WITH MODESTY TODAY ...THAT MAN LAST NIGHT LOOKED LIKE TROUBLE TO ME— *BAD* TROUBLE

WE'LL BE BACK FOR LUNCH, MARJ...

...IT'S ON'Y A LITTLE BUSINESS CHAT

WILLIE! WHAT—?

BELT UP AN' GET OUT A CLEAN SHIRT FOR ME, THERE'S A GOOD GIRL

280

MODESTY BLAISE by PETER O'DONNELL

ANSWER ME DAMN YOU, WILLIE! WHO *IS* THIS MAN GABRIEL? AND WHY ARE YOU CARRYING THOSE... THOSE *KNIVES*?

HE'S NOT— LEAVE THEM, WILLIE, AND LET'S GET GOING... WE WON'T HAVE ANY TROUBLE TODAY

HIS MASTER'S VOICE... WHEN SHE SAYS 'FROG' YOU JUMP, HUH?

IT'S A WINNING SYSTEM, MARJ— ONCE YOU'VE GOT LUCKY YOU STICK WITH IT

281

MODESTY BLAISE by PETER O'DONNELL

HERE'S WHERE WE TURN OFF THE HIGHWAY, WILLIE

RIGHT

YOU DON'T RECKON WE'RE STICKING OUR NECKS OUT THEN, PRINCESS?

NOT YET... WE'VE BEEN SUMMONED SO GABRIEL CAN WARN US OFF, THE WAY HE DID ONCE BEFORE IN THE OLD DAYS

A FEW MINUTES LATER...

THEY'RE HERE, GABRIEL— ON THE DOT

WHAT ELSE? SHE'S NO FOOL

282

MODESTY BLAISE by PETER O'DONNELL

MODESTY BLAISE by PETER O'DONNELL

MODESTY BLAISE by PETER O'DONNELL

MODESTY BLAISE by PETER O'DONNELL

MODESTY BLAISE by PETER O'DONNELL

MODESTY BLAISE by PETER O'DONNELL

MODESTY BLAISE by PETER O'DONNELL

MODESTY BLAISE by PETER O'DONNELL

MODESTY BLAISE by PETER O'DONNELL

Lost in total concentration, Willie Garvin whispers caressingly under his breath as the long minutes creep by...

COME ON, SWEETIE... AH THERE'S A PET... EASY NOW, HONEY GIRL... ROLL OVER FOR WILLIE

AHH... THAT'S ME LITTLE BEAUTY!

SHE'S DONE, PRINCESS

YOU DON'T CRACK THEM, WILLIE LOVE— YOU SEDUCE THEM

MODESTY BLAISE by PETER O'DONNELL

MICRO-FILM RECORDS...

LOVELY

PUT THEM IN YOUR PACK AND LET'S GET GOING, WILLIE

'OLD ON, PRINCESS... LOOKS LIKE WE GOT PEOPLE TROUBLE

MODESTY BLAISE by PETER O'DONNELL

THAT'LL BE GABRIEL'S LOT WAITING FOR US — THEY'LL 'AVE FOUND OUR CAR, TOO

I'LL DRAW THEM... YOU FIND YOUR OWN WAY OUT AND GET CLEAR WITH THOSE MICRO-FILMS

NO, WILLIE... THE ONLY SURE WAY OUT NOW IS ACROSS COUNTRY ON FOOT, AND YOU'RE STRONG ON THAT

THAT WAY ROUND? *YOU* COULD TAKE THE FILMS, AN'—

WHAT'S YOUR WAY THEN?

WHEN I'VE KEPT THEM BUSY A WHILE, I'LL TRY TO TAKE *THEIR* CAR... SO I'LL BE WAITING FOR YOU IN TREMONT WITH ANY LUCK

MODESTY BLAISE by PETER O'DONNELL

YOU GOT ANYTHING, PREMM? THIS SIDE WE GOT SOMEONE CLIMBING DOWN FROM A WINDOW... LOOKS LIKE THE BLAISE WOMAN

YEAH, YOU THREE STAY THAT SIDE AND WATCH FOR GARVIN... WE'LL PICK HER UP OKAY, NORSTENE AND CREVIER HAVE GOT HER BRACKETED RIGHT BETWEEN THEM

MODESTY BLAISE
by PETER O'DONNELL

MODESTY BLAISE
by PETER O'DONNELL

MODESTY BLAISE
by PETER O'DONNELL

MODESTY BLAISE
by PETER O'DONNELL

MODESTY BLAISE
by PETER O'DONNELL

The cordon passes Modesty by

TRY FOR THEIR CAR NOW...THEY'LL HAVE MINE WELL COVERED

ACROSS THE GROUNDS, NORSTENE RECOVERS FROM THE STUNNING EFFECT OF THE KONGO

I'LL KILL THAT CLEVER BITCH...

303

MODESTY BLAISE
by PETER O'DONNELL

CAN'T GET HIM CLEAN WHILE HE'S IN THE CAR...

ENGINE'S RUNNING... STOP THAT AND IT OUGHT TO BRING HIM OUT FOR A LOOK UNDER THE BONNET

304

MODESTY BLAISE
by PETER O'DONNELL

With the exhaust blocked, the idling engine falters then stops... and the starter labours in vain

SHE'S DEAD! NOW WHAT THE HELL—?

RICCO STEPS OUT OF THE CAR... AND GLANCES BACK

305

MODESTY BLAISE
by PETER O'DONNELL

As Ricco is smashed to the ground, Norstene appears

AHH!

GOT TO GET OUT FAST NOW—AND TO HELL WITH THE NOISE!

THE SHARP REPORT OF THE AUTOMATIC ECHOES THROUGH THE WOODS

306

MODESTY BLAISE
by PETER O'DONNELL

NORSTENE! WHAT HAPPENED?

SHE... GOT CLEAR

GET HER CAR AND GO AFTER HER! I'LL TAKE NORSTENE INTO THE PHOENIX... AND PHONE GABRIEL

MY GOD, HE'LL HAVE THE HIDE OFF US FOR THIS...

307

MODESTY BLAISE
by PETER O'DONNELL

As DR. VARLEY ATTENDS TO NORSTENE

YEAH, I–I GUESS THAT'S IT, GABRIEL ...THE BOYS HAVE GONE AFTER BLAISE, BUT WE FIGURE IT'S GARVIN WHO'S GOT THE MICRO-FILM RECORDS

WHAT'S THIS YOU HAD ON THE WOUND?

UH? HER SWEATER... IT WAS THERE... I DON'T KNOW HOW

308

LOOK, HOLD IT, GABRIEL– YEAH, I *KNOW* WE LET THE DAME BEAT US–*BUT I JUST GOT AN ANGLE!* LISTEN THERE'S THIS SWEATER SHE WAS WEARING...

MODESTY BLAISE
by PETER O'DONNELL

Two CARS SCREAM THROUGH THE NIGHT . . .

AFTER ME IN MY OWN CAR... AND IT'S FASTER

WONDER WHERE THE HELL THIS ROAD COMES OUT...?

U.S. BORDER IN THREE MILES, AND NO TURN-OFFS – YOU DON'T TAKE HER SOON AND WE LOSE HER, CREVIER!

TELL IT TO THE CAR!

309

MODESTY BLAISE
by PETER O'DONNELL

HOLD IT! THE BORDER POST!

In THE LEADING CAR, MODESTY KEEPS HER FOOT DOWN

HOLY, JUMPIN'–! DID YOU SEE WHAT SHE WAS *WEARING?*

SHE WASN'T! MUST HAVE BEEN SOME PARTY, MIKE! YOU'D BETTER–AH NO, SHE'S STOPPING

310

MODESTY BLAISE
by PETER O'DONNELL

LADY, YOU'RE IN TROUBLE — RIGHT UP TO YOUR EARS

NOT SO DEEP AS I WAS IN JUST NOW

ON THE CANADIAN SIDE OF THE BORDER, GABRIEL'S MEN TURN BACK

YOU'LL WANT THIS FOR THE TIME BEING — CAN I TALK TO SOMEBODY WHO CAN TALK TO SOMEBODY IN CANADIAN SECURITY ABOUT ME?

I WOULDN'T KNOW... THAT'S A BIG QUESTION WITH A SLOW ANSWER, LADY

MODESTY BLAISE
by PETER O'DONNELL

THIS IDEA WORKS — WHETHER THE BOYS CATCH BLAISE OR NOT, GABRIEL! GARVIN'S GOT THE MICROFILMS, SO IT'S HIM WE WANT...

AND I KNOW GARVIN! IF HE RECKONS WE'VE KILLED HER, WE WON'T HAVE TO GO LOOKING FOR HIM ...HE'LL COME TO US!

WE GOT HER SWEATER WITH BLOOD ALL OVER IT, AND WE CAN—

I DON'T NEED DIAGRAMS, LERI — DO IT

MODESTY BLAISE
by PETER O'DONNELL

AT THE HOTEL LUMINOR, IN THE EARLY HOURS, MARJORIE LANIER WAKES

WILLIE?

STAY QUIET AND YOU DON'T GET HURT... I GOT A MESSAGE FOR YOU TO TELL GARVIN — IT'S FROM GABRIEL, YOU GOT THAT NAME?

YOU GIVE GARVIN THIS, AND YOU TELL HIM WE DID IT SLOW, REAL SLOW...

MODESTY'S BLOOD-STAINED SWEATER, RIPPED AND CUT NOW

MODESTY BLAISE
by PETER O'DONNELL

GABRIEL'S PLACE — 'LAKESIDE'

I COULD HIRE TOUGHER INVALIDS... YOU LET A HUNDRED AND THIRTY POUNDS OF WOMAN MAKE MUSH OUT OF YOU

WE COULDN'T GO INTO THE STATES AFTER HER—

IT DOESN'T MATTER NOW, AND THAT MAKES YOU LUCKY. BLAISE IS PINNED DOWN THERE IN BIG TROUBLE WITH THE POLICE...

...SO LERI'S MOVE WITH GARVIN'S GIRL IS GOING TO WORK OUT OKAY FOR US

MODESTY BLAISE
by PETER O'DONNELL

WHAT ANGLE DO YOU FIGURE BLAISE WAS WORKING, GABRIEL?

I DON'T KNOW OR CARE... I JUST WANT THE MICROFILMS

GARVIN WILL HAVE CACHED THEM, BUT ONCE WE GET *HIM*, HE'LL TELL US WHERE... YOU'D LIKE TO MAKE HIM, RICCO, HUH?

OKAY, GABRIEL— THAT DAME OF GARVIN'S BELIEVES WE'VE KILLED THE BLAISE WOMAN... AND *HE'LL* BELIEVE IT TOO

THEN WE'LL HAVE SOME ACTION IN A FEW HOURS

315

MODESTY BLAISE
by PETER O'DONNELL

MODESTY? SAM BARTH HERE. THE C.I.A. PEOPLE HAVE BEEN ON TO ME AND I'VE CLEARED YOU WITH THEM—

ANY NEWS OF WILLIE?

IN A UNITED STATES POLICE H.Q.

NOT YET, MODESTY— WHAT GOES ON?

MEET ME AT THE LUMINOR IN A COUPLE OF HOURS AND I'LL TELL YOU— WILLIE SHOULD HAVE SHOWED UP THERE BY THEN

THANKS, CAPTAIN, THIS COULD HAVE TAKEN A WEEK... YOU'RE A NICE MAN

I JUST ENJOY GETTING A LOT OF BIG-SHOTS OUT OF BED, MA'AM

316

MODESTY BLAISE
by PETER O'DONNELL

At THE HOTEL LUMINOR, SOON AFTER DAWN

'ALLO, MARJ, IT'S ONLY ME— IS MODESTY BACK YET?

HEY,...! WHAT'S UP, MARJ? BLIMEY, YOU'RE SHAKIN' ALL OVER

A M-MAN CAME... HE WAS... HORRIBLE!

HE-HE TOLD ME TO GIVE YOU A M-MESSAGE ... FROM SOMEONE CALLED... GABRIEL

GABRIEL?

317

MODESTY BLAISE
by PETER O'DONNELL

YOU GOT IT WRONG SOMEWHERE, MARJ—MODESTY WOULDN'T KICK OFF THAT EASY

MODESTY'S DEAD! DON'T YOU UNDERSTAND? THEY'VE KILLED HER!

NO... SHE DIDN'T! THE MAN SAID TO TELL YOU FROM GABRIEL— IT WAS SLOW, REAL *SLOW*! I'M SCARED, WILLIE— SCARED FOR *YOU*!

LOOK! HE-HE BROUGHT *THAT*! IT'S HER SWEATER! IT'S S-SOAKED IN BLOOD... HORRIBLE HOLES IN IT...

318

MODESTY BLAISE
by PETER O'DONNELL

FOR GOD'S SAKE COME AWAY WITH ME, WILLIE! THEY'VE KILLED MODESTY, AND THEY'LL KILL YOU, TOO!

YOU'LL 'AVE TO EXCUSE ME, MARJ... I GOT SOMETHING TO DO

WHERE ARE YOU GOING?

WILLIE! PLEASE!

MODESTY BLAISE
by PETER O'DONNELL

IN MODESTY'S SUITE

YOU CAN'T HELP MODESTY NOW! LOOK, WE CAN BE OUT OF TOWN IN AN HOUR—

DON'T KEEP TALKIN', MARJ, PLEASE

I WANT YOU TO RING A BLOKE CALLED SAM BARTH—'ERE'S THE NUMBER

GET SAM ROUND 'ERE, TELL 'IM WHAT'S 'APPENED, AND SAY I'VE LEFT A BOX OF MICRO-FILM AT JACEY'S ALL-NIGHT GARAGE FOR 'IM TO COLLECT

MODESTY BLAISE
by PETER O'DONNELL

WHAT ARE YOU *DOING*?

JUST WANTED MODESTY'S OTHER GUN— THE COLT '32

SHE ALWAYS SAYS—

SHE ALWAYS USED TO SAY I COULDN'T HIT THE FLOOR WITH A GUN— AN' SHE WAS RIGHT, MARJ

STILL, I'D LIKE TO 'AVE IT ALONG

MODESTY BLAISE
by PETER O'DONNELL

IMPASSIVE AND METHODICAL, WILLIE GARVIN CHECKS THE COLT, THEN HIS KNIVES

YOU'RE GOING TO GET YOURSELF KILLED FOR HER! THAT WON'T BRING HER BACK!

BUT YOU DON'T *CARE!* YOU WERE ALWAYS CRAZY ABOUT HER, WEREN'T YOU?

NOT THE WAY YOU MEAN, MARJ... BIGGER'N THAT

WELL, I GOT TO GO ALONG NOW... SORRY ABOUT EVERYTHING

NO!

MODESTY BLAISE
by PETER O'DONNELL

MODESTY BLAISE
by PETER O'DONNELL

MODESTY BLAISE
by PETER O'DONNELL

MODESTY BLAISE
by PETER O'DONNELL

MODESTY BLAISE
by PETER O'DONNELL

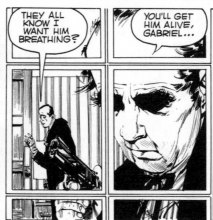

TIME YOU BIG EXECS GOT BACK TO A LITTLE FIELD WORK... IT SHOULDN'T BE TOO TOUGH FOR EIGHT OF YOU TO TAKE GARVIN

THEY ALL KNOW I WANT HIM BREATHING?

YOU'LL GET HIM ALIVE, GABRIEL...

...HE'S GOT A HUNDRED-FIFTY YARDS CLEAR GROUND TO CROSS, WHICHEVER WAY HE COMES — AND WE GOT MEN AT WINDOWS EVERY SIDE, ALL GOOD GUNS

327

MODESTY BLAISE
by PETER O'DONNELL

*M*ODESTY REACHES THE HOTEL LUMINOR

SAM! WHAT'S GOING ON?

LOOK! *NOW* WILL YOU QUIT GIVING ME THIS CRAZY STORY ABOUT MODESTY BEING DEAD! I *TOLD* YOU SHE PHONED ME!

HE... THE MAN... SAID YOU WERE *DEAD* — WE *BELIEVED* IT! WILLIE —

TAKE IT QUIETLY, MARJ, FROM THE TOP NOW — WHAT HAPPENED?

328

MODESTY BLAISE
by PETER O'DONNELL

*M*ARJ STUMBLES THROUGH HER STORY...

AND... WHEN WILLIE SAW YOUR SWEATER... ALL... LIKE *THAT*... HE–HE THOUGHT THEY'D K-KILLED YOU...

HE WENT... AND HE TOOK YOUR OTHER GUN —

GUN? WILLIE?

HE'S COLD BERSERK, SAM! HE'S GONE FOR A SHOWDOWN! *AND THAT'S JUST WHAT THEY WANT HIM TO DO!*

329

MODESTY BLAISE
by PETER O'DONNELL

I'LL GET A POLICE SQUAD TO MEET US ON THE ROAD OUT OF TOWN

HOW LONG HAS WILLIE BEEN GONE, MARJ?

I–I DON'T KNOW... AN HOUR...?

HOW MANY MEN HAS GABRIEL GOT?

EIGHT, NINE... *ENOUGH!* AND ALL LAYING FOR WILLIE — HE'LL NEVER EVEN GET INTO THE HOUSE ALIVE!

HE'LL GET IN... AND HE'LL STAY ALIVE LONG ENOUGH TO KILL GABRIEL... THAT'S ALL HE CARES ABOUT NOW

330

MODESTY BLAISE
by PETER O'DONNELL

Two guns fire as one...

HE'S GOT CREVIER!

STREWTH... RIGHT ON THE 'OOTER... THAT'S A GIGGLE, EH, PRINCESS? 'OO SAID I COULDN'T 'IT A BARN STANDING INSIDE IT...?

335

MODESTY BLAISE
by PETER O'DONNELL

WATCH THAT DOOR! BLAST HIM WHEN HE SHOWS!

But Willie Garvin has already doubled back on his tracks

WE GOT TWO SO FAR, PRINCESS... RECKON THE OTHERS'LL BE WATCHING THE 'ALL NOW

BETTER NOT PUSH ME LUCK TRYING A SHOT THIS TIME...

336

MODESTY BLAISE
by PETER O'DONNELL

Gabriel's men watch the room where Willie Garvin should be...

LERI! GET OUTSIDE AND TAKE HIM FROM BEHIND!

RIGHT

But Willie is a long jump ahead

337

MODESTY BLAISE
by PETER O'DONNELL

I HAD NORSTENE WATCH THE LOWER WINDOW, AND LERI DIDN'T COME OUT!

THEN GARVIN GOT TO HIM FIRST...

WATCH LERI'S ROOM! GARVIN'S THERE NOW!

Willie heaves Leri's unconscious bulk on to a trolley

WE'LL GIVE 'EM SOMETHING TO SHOOT AT, EH, LERI?

338

MODESTY BLAISE
by PETER O'DONNELL

MODESTY BLAISE
by PETER O'DONNELL

MODESTY BLAISE
by PETER O'DONNELL

MODESTY BLAISE
by PETER O'DONNELL

MODESTY BLAISE
by PETER O'DONNELL

343

With bullet-wounds draining the last of his strength now, Willie Garvin drags himself from room to room of the upper floor

GABRIEL!

COME ON! JUST YOU AN' ME NOW!

MODESTY BLAISE
by PETER O'DONNELL

344

His whole band of eight men wiped out by Willie Garvin, Gabriel is in flight...

GABRIEL...! YOU **GOT** TO BE 'ERE...! I KEPT A KNIFE FOR YOU...

MODESTY BLAISE
by PETER O'DONNELL

345

Eyes glazing, Willie hears the sound of the little speedboat racing away across the lake...

LOST 'IM, PRINCESS ...SORRY... NEVER WAS MUCH GOOD WITHOUT YOU...

MODESTY BLAISE
by PETER O'DONNELL

With a police squad behind them, Modesty and Sam Barth scream down the road to 'Lakeside'

YOU'VE GOT TO RECKON ON THE WORST, MODESTY, THEY WERE **WAITING** FOR WILLIE...

THEY COULD HAVE KNOCKED HIM OFF AN HOUR AGO AND BE QUIETLY HAVING BREAKFAST NOW—**MY GOD, THERE'S A TRUCK HALFWAY THROUGH THE WALL!**

I TOLD YOU WILLIE WOULD GET IN...

346

Modesty BLAISE
IN THE BEGINNING
by PETER O'DONNELL and JIM HOLDAWAY

IN THE WAR'S FINAL MONTHS OF CHAOS A SMALL REFUGEE CHILD SLIPPED AWAY FROM A PRISON CAMP IN GREECE

THE HAND SHE HAD CLUNG TO THROUGH AN ETERNITY OF HARDSHIP AND FLIGHT WAS COLD NOW... AND SHE WAS ALONE

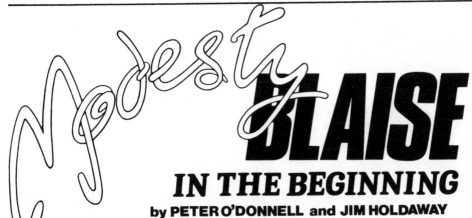

SHOCK MADE MEMORY A SHAPELESS BLUR OF HORROR. THE CHILD NO LONGER KNEW HER OWN NAME. SHE ONLY KNEW THAT SHE MUST ESCAPE... AND SURVIVE ANOTHER DAY AS SHE HAD SURVIVED SO MANY YESTERDAYS

1

BY INSTINCT THE CHILD KEPT GOING SOUTH, THROUGH TURKEY, AWAY FROM THE WAR. IN GOOD WEATHER SHE LIVED WILD IN THE FORESTS...

WHEN WINTER CAME SHE MADE HER HOME IN A CRANNY OF SOME SMALL VILLAGE, LIKE A WILD CAT. TO EAT, SHE WOULD WORK OR BEG...

...OR STEAL. ALL FEAR AND SORROW HAD LONG SINCE BEEN BURNT OUT OF HER. SHE WAS HIGHLY SKILLED IN THE ART OF SURVIVAL NOW

2.

THE CHILD HAD TRAVELLED ALONE FOR A LONG TIME WHEN AT LAST, WITH MANY OTHER REFUGEES, SHE CROSSED THE BORDER INTO PERSIA

HERE THERE WERE CAMPS FOR SUCH PEOPLE—FOR THOSE WITHOUT A COUNTRY, WITHOUT BELONGINGS, WITHOUT HOPE. BUT THEY WERE SAD, GRIM PLACES

SHE SELDOM STAYED LONG IN A CAMP, BUT WOULD MOVE ON— TO STEAL IN THE CITY BAZAARS, PERHAPS, OR TO ROAM FOR A WHILE WITH A NOMAD TRIBE

3

IT WAS IN A D.P. CAMP THAT SHE FIRST MET THE OLD MAN—AND SAW HIM ROBBED OF HIS MEAGRE RATION OF FOOD

STRANGELY, THE CHILD REACTED AS SHE WOULD HAVE REACTED FOR HERSELF. HER SWIFT ATTACK WAS FEROCIOUS

THE THIEF FLED, HIS ARM RIPPED BY THE WEAPON SHE CARRIED—A LONG NAIL, HONED SHARP AND BOUND WITH WIRE TO A WOODEN HAFT

THE MAN COULD NEVER SURVIVE ALONE...BUT SHE KNEW SHE COULD EASILY TAKE CARE OF HIM, FOR SHE WAS QUITE OLD NOW— AT LEAST TWELVE

SO BEGAN A STRANGE FRIENDSHIP. HE HAD BEEN SOMETHING CALLED A PROFESSOR, AND KNEW EVERYTHING

THEY LEFT THE CAMP, AND THROUGH A LONG SUMMER HE BEGAN TO TEACH HER. BUT FIRST HE GAVE HER A NAME, MODESTY—AND CHUCKLED AS HE GAVE IT

OFTEN SHE STOLE BOOKS, SO THAT THE OLD MAN COULD TEACH HER MORE. SHE SOAKED UP KNOWLEDGE EAGERLY. AND HE WAS VERY CONTENT

FOR FOUR YEARS THIS STRANGE PAIR WANDERED LIKE GYPSIES THROUGH THE MIDDLE EAST. AT TIMES THERE WAS DANGER... BUT TO MODESTY THIS WAS NOTHING NEW

SHE CHOSE HER SECOND NAME FROM A STORY HE TOLD HER— ABOUT A KING CALLED ARTHUR, HIS KNIGHTS OF THE ROUND TABLE, AND A MAGICIAN, MERLIN, WHOSE TUTOR HAD BEEN NAMED BLAISE

Modesty Blaise

AMBITION BURNT FIERCELY IN MODESTY BLAISE NOW. TANGIER, SHE KNEW, WAS A CITY WHERE ONE COULD QUICKLY GROW RICH. THAT JOURNEY WAS THE LONGEST THEY HAD EVER MADE

ONLY FIFTY MILES FROM THE CITY, THE OLD MAN QUIETLY DIED. SHE BURIED HIM IN THE DESERT, AND WEPT FOR THE FIRST TIME IN HER MEMORY

THREE MONTHS LATER SHE WAS SPINNING A WHEEL FOR A SMALL-TIME TANGIER GANG LED BY A MAN CALLED LOUCHE. SHE LEARNED MANY THINGS IN THE NEXT TWO YEARS...

WHEN LOUCHE WAS KILLED IN A GANG BATTLE IT WAS MODESTY BLAISE WHO RALLIED THE GROUP AND TOOK OVER AS LEADER

SHE HAD THE SKILL AND THE WILL TO MAKE HER PLANS WORK. WITHIN TWO YEARS THE GROUP HAD BECOME *The Network*, OPERATING THROUGH BRANCHES IN MANY COUNTRIES

SHE WAS, AS FAR AS SHE KNEW, ONLY TWENTY—AND THE NAME OF MODESTY BLAISE WAS ALREADY NOTORIOUS. BUT NOTHING COULD EVER BE PROVED AGAINST HER

THE NETWORK DEALT IN MANY CRIMES, BUT NEVER DRUGS OR VICE. MODESTY BLAISE LOATHED HUMAN DEGRADATION AND THOSE WHO DEALT IN IT. FOR THIS SHE WOULD KILL . . .

IT WAS IN SAIGON THAT SHE FIRST SAW WILLIE GARVIN—IN THAI-STYLE COMBAT. OF LETHAL SKILLS, HE WAS GUTTER-BRED WITH A MIND CLOUDED BY UNREASONING HATRED

A WEEK LATER SHE BOUGHT HIM OUT OF JAIL—WITHOUT STRINGS. TO A DAZED WILLIE GARVIN SHE SEEMED A PRINCESS.... AND "PRINCESS" HE CALLED HER FROM THAT TIME ON

WITHIN SIX MONTHS A NEW WILLIE GARVIN WAS BORN—A MAN OF CHEERFUL CONFIDENCE, SHARP INTELLIGENCE, AND ALL HIS OLD CRIMINAL SKILLS . . .

SOON HE WAS MODESTY'S RIGHT ARM IN RUNNING *The Network*. BOTH WERE UNIQUE, BOTH ORIGINALS. THEY LEARNT MUCH FROM ONE ANOTHER

THROUGH SIX YEARS WILLIE GARVIN SERVED "The Princess". TOGETHER THEY SCHEMED, FOUGHT, BLED, TENDED EACH OTHER'S HURTS... AND GREW VERY RICH

THERE CAME A TIME WHEN, WITH AMBITION FULFILLED, MODESTY COULD SPLIT UP *The Network* AMONG HER SECTION CHIEFS AND RETIRE TO A LIFE OF EASE

SHE BOUGHT A PENTHOUSE IN LONDON—AND WILLIE GARVIN, ALSO RICH FOR LIFE, BOUGHT AN OLD-WORLD PUB BY THE RIVER THAMES

BUT AFTER THE YEARS OF DANGER THEY FOUND LIFE DULL AND INSIPID WITHOUT THAT HEADY SPICE. ONE SHREWD MAN HAD FORESEEN THIS... SIR GERALD TARRANT, OF BRITISH INTELLIGENCE

THROUGH TARRANT, A NEW CHAPTER BEGAN FOR MODESTY BLAISE. HE ASKED HER HELP, AND WILLIE'S, IN A MISSION REQUIRING INTIMATE KNOWLEDGE OF THE UNDERWORLD. AND SO THEY WENT INTO ACTION ANEW . . .

THERE HAVE BEEN OTHER HARD, DANGEROUS MISSIONS SINCE THEN FOR THIS UNIQUE PAIR. BUT THEY ARE NOT EMPLOYEES. THEY TAKE NO PAY, NO ORDERS. AND NOT ALL THEIR EXPLOITS STEM FROM TARRANT

LONG EXPOSURE TO THE CURRENTS OF DANGER SEEMS TO HAVE MADE THEM HUMAN MAGNETS, ATTRACTING TROUBLE. AND THEY ARE CONTENT FOR THIS TO BE SO

In the Beginning was written and drawn in 1966 to serve as an introduction for those newspapers that picked up the Modesty Blaise strip in the middle of its run.